CorelCAD 2023 Basics Tutorial

Tutorial Books

Contents

Introduction to CorelCAD 2023

In this chapter, you will learn about:

- **CorelCAD user interface**
- **Customizing user interface**

System requirements

The following are system requirements for running CorelCAD smoothly on your system.

- Microsoft Windows 11 or Windows 10 (Version 21H1 or later) (64 - bit only).
- Intel Core 2 Duo, or AMD® Athlon™ x2 Dual-Core processor
- 4 GB RAM (8 GB or more recommended)
- 1.5 GB available hard disk space
- 3D Graphics accelerator card with OpenGL version 1.4 (OpenGL version 3.2 or better recommended)
- 1280 x 768 screen resolution (1920 x 1080 (Full HD) recommended)

Starting CorelCAD 2023

To start **CorelCAD 2023**, double-click the **CorelCAD 2023** icon on your Desktop (or) click **Start > All apps > CorelCAD 2023 > CorelCAD 2023**.

CorelCAD user interface

When you double-click the CorelCAD 2023 icon on the desktop, the CorelCAD 2023 Start screen appears. On the Quick Access Toolbar, click the **New** button. Next, select a template from the **Specify Template** dialog and click **Open** to open a new drawing file. The drawing file consists of a graphics window, ribbon, menu bar, toolbars, command window, and other screen components, depending on the workspace that you have selected.

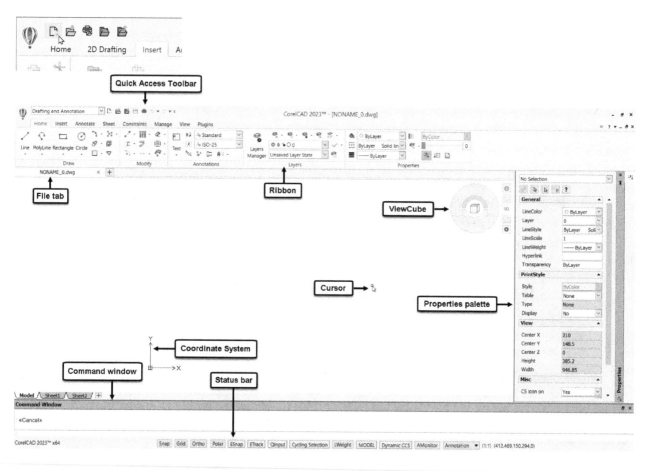

Changing the Color theme

CorelCAD 2023 is available in two different color themes: **Dark** and **Light**. You can change the Color theme by using the **Options** dialog. Click the right mouse button and select **Options** from the shortcut menu. On the **Options** dialog, click the **System Options** tab and expand the **Display > User Interface style** node. Next, select Light or Dark option and click OK;

the CorelCAD 2023 message box appears showing that the user interface style is updated after the program is restarted. Click **Close** and restart the program.

 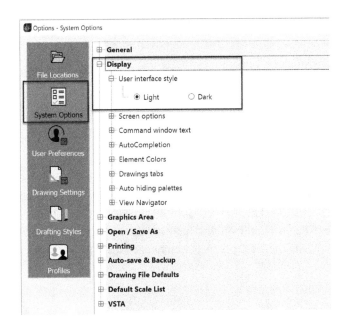

Workspaces in CorelCAD

There are four workspaces available in CorelCAD: **Drafting & Annotation**, **3D Modeling**, **CAD General**, and **Classic**. The **Drafting & Annotation** workspace is used to create 2D drawings. You can enable this workspace by using the **Workspace** drop-down on the top-left corner.

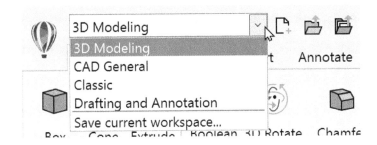

Drafting & Annotation Workspace

This workspace has all the tools to create a 2D drawing. It has a ribbon located at the top of the screen. The ribbon is arranged in a hierarchy of tabs, panels, and tools. Panels such as **Draw**, **Modify**, and **Layers** consist of tools that are grouped based on their usage. Panels, in turn, are grouped into various tabs. For example, the panels, such as **Draw**, **Modify**, and **Layers**, are located in the **Home** tab.

3D Modeling Workspace

This workspace are used to create 3D models. It includes all the tools required for creating 3D models. By default, the **Home** tab is activated in the ribbon. From this tab, you can access the tools for creating and editing solids and meshes, modifying the model display, working with coordinate systems, and sectioning 3D models.

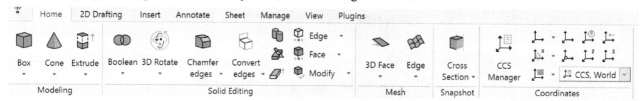

Application Menu

The **Application Menu** appears when you click on the icon located at the top left corner of the window. The **Application Menu** consists of a list of options such as **New**, **Open**, **Save**, and **Print** on the left side. Place the pointer on any one of the options on the left side; a list of additional options is displayed on the right side. You can see a list of recently opened documents on the right side. In addition to that, there are three buttons, **Options, About,** and **Exit** located at the bottom of the **Application Menu**. You can use the **Options** button to open the **Options** dialog. In this dialog, you can specify various settings related to display, printing, and user preferences.

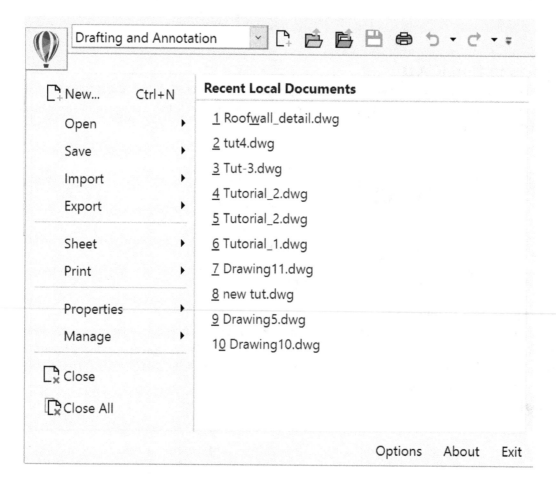

Quick Access Toolbar

The Quick Access Toolbar is located at the top left corner of the window and helps you to access commands quickly. It consists of commonly used commands such as **New**, **Save**, **Open**, **Open Sheet Set**, and **Save As**,

File tabs

The File tabs are located below the ribbon. You can switch between different drawing files by using the file tabs. Also, you can open a new file by using the + button, easily.

Graphics Window

The Graphics window is the blank space located below the file tabs. You can draw objects and create 3D graphics in the graphics window.

View Navigator

The View Navigator located at the top-right corner of the graphics window. You can turn ON of OFF the View Navigator by clicking **View > ViewTiles > View Navigator** on the ribbon. The View Navigator allows you to switch between the standard and isometric views. Using the View Navigator, you can set the orientation of the model. For example, if you want to change the orientation of the model to top view, then place the upper segment of the inner ring, as shown; the Top message appears. Click on the highlighted segment of the ring to change the view orientation. Likewise, if you want to change the orientation to SW Isometric, then place the pointer on the bottom left segment of the outer ring; the SW Isometric message appears. Click on the highlighted segment to change the view orientation to SW Isometric. Also, notice the cube inside the two rings. Its position changes as you change the view orientation.

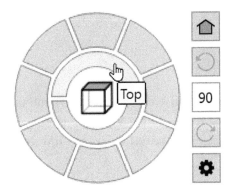
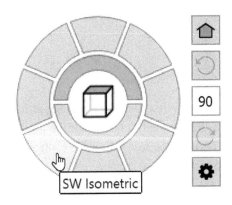

Likewise, you can click on the different sectors of the two rings to switch to the respective views, as shown.

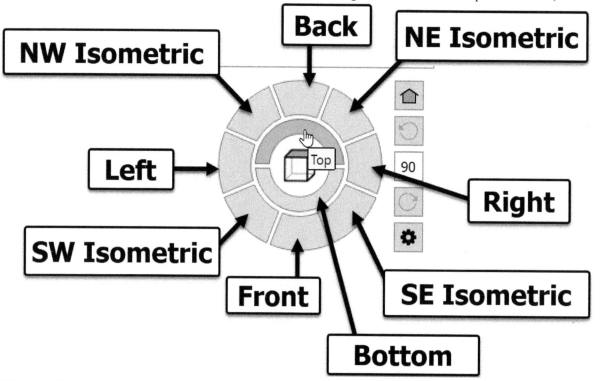

Click the **Home** button located at the top-right corner of the View Navigator to change the view orientation to Home view.

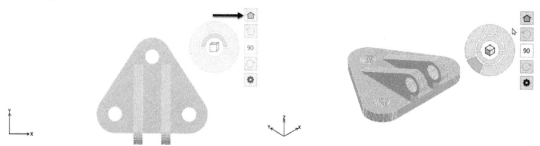

By default, the SW Isometric view is set as home view. However, you can set a different view as the Home view. To do this, change the orientation of the model by clicking on anyone of the sectors of the **View Navigator**. Next, click the **Gear** button located on the right side of the View Navigator. Next, select the **Set Current View as Home** option.

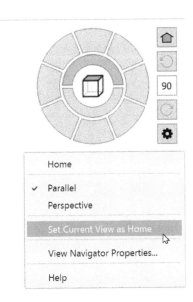

Command Window

The command window is located below the graphics window. It is effortless to execute a command using the command window. You can just type the first letter of a command, and it lists all the commands starting with that letter. It helps you to activate commands very quickly and increases your productivity.

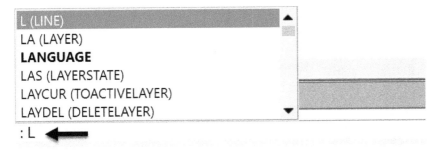

Also, the command window shows the current state of the drawing. It shows various prompts while working with any command. These prompts are a series of steps needed to execute a command successfully. For example, when you activate the LINE command, the command window displays a prompt, "Specify start point." You need to click in the graphics window to specify the start point of the line. After defining the start t point, the prompt, "Specify next point" appears. Now, you need to determine the next end of the line. It is recommended that you should always have a look at the command window to know the next step while executing a command.

Status Bar

Status Bar is located at the bottom of the CorelCAD window. It contains many buttons which help you to create a drawing very easily. You can turn ON or OFF these buttons just by clicking on them. The buttons available on the status bar are briefly discussed in the following section.

Button	Description

(280.368,235.809,0) **Coordinate Display**	It displays the drawing coordinates when you move the pointer in the graphics window.
Snap	The Snap button aligns the pointer only with the Grid points. When you turn ON this button, the pointer will be able to select only the Grid points.
Grid	It turns the Grid display ON or OFF. You can set the spacing between the grid lines by right-clicking on the **Grid** button and selecting the **Settings** option. Next, specify the **Horizontal display spacing** and **Vertical display spacing** on the **Options** dialog and click **OK**. You can use the grid lines along with the Snap Mode to draw objects quickly and accurately.
Ortho	It turns the Ortho Mode ON or OFF. When the Ortho Mode is ON, only horizontal or vertical lines can be drawn.
Polar	This button turns ON or OFF the Polar Guides. When the Polar Guides are turned ON, you can draw lines quickly at regular angular increments, such as 5, 10, 15, 23, 30, 45, or 90 degrees. You will notice that a trace line is displayed when the pointer is at a particular angular increment.

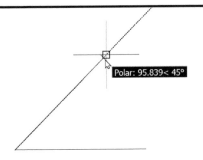

You can set the angular increment by right-clicking on the **Polar** button and selecting the **Settings** option. Next, select the required angle from the **Incremental angles for Polar guides display** drop-down. Click **OK** on the **Options** dialog.

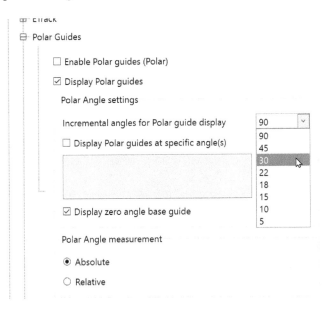

ESnap	This button turns ON or OFF the ESnap mode. When this mode is turned ON, you can easily select the key points of objects such as endpoints, midpoint, and center point.

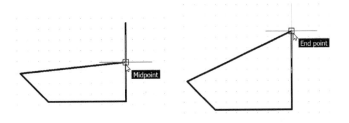

ETrack	This button is used to turn ON or OFF the ETrack mode. When this mode is turned ON, you can easily select points by using the trace lines originating from the key points.

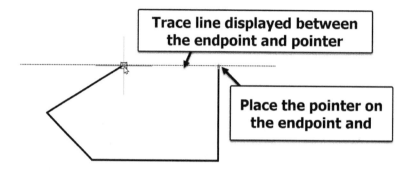

Trace line displayed between the endpoint and pointer

Place the pointer on the endpoint and

Dynamic CCS	This button turns ON/OFF the Dynamic CCS. When the Dynamic CCS is turned ON, you can draw and create objects on any face of a 3D Model, dynamically.

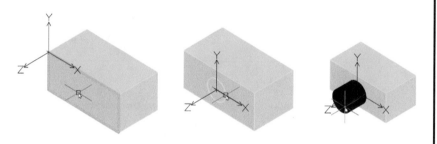

QInput	This button turns ON or OFF the QInput mode. When this mode is turned ON, a dynamic input box is attached to the pointer along with a prompt. You can directly enter a value in the dynamic input box. You can use Dynamic Input in place of the command window.

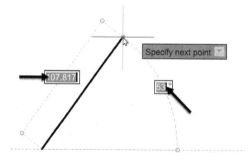

Specify next point

107.817

53

LWeight	This button turns ON or OFF the lineweight. Line weight is the thickness of objects. You can set the thickness of objects by specifying the lineweight. If the Lineweight is turned OFF, the objects are displayed with the default thickness. 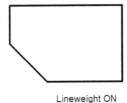 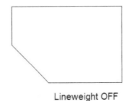
Cycling Selection	This button turns ON or OFF the Cycling Selection. It is beneficial while selecting overlapped objects. Turn ON the selection cycling and click on the overlapping objects. Select the required object from the **Cycling Selection** list. 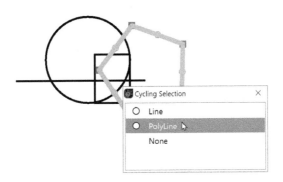
AMonitor	This button turns the Annotation Monitor ON or OFF. The Annotation Monitor checks whether the annotations are attached to their respective objects. When an annotation is not connected to any object, it displays an error message. 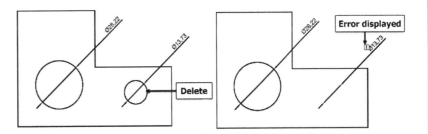
Annotation	This drop-down the size of annotative objects. Annotative objects are dimensions, texts, notes, and other objects which can be sized as per the drawing scale.

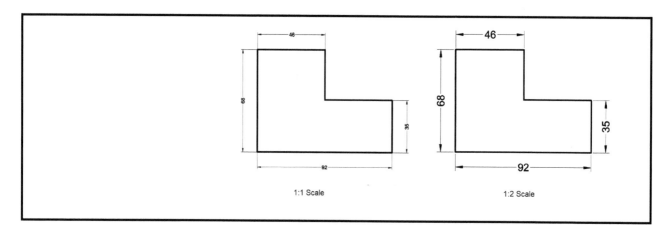

1:1 Scale   1:2 Scale

Menu Bar

The Menu Bar is available only in the **Classic** workspace. Select the **Classic** option from the Workspace drop-down available on the Quick Access Toolbar; the Menu bar appears at the top of the window just below the title bar. It contains various menus such as File, Edit, View, Insert, Format, Tools, Draw, Dimensions, Modify, and so on. Clicking on any of the words on the Menu Bar displays a menu. The menu contains various tools and options. There are also sub-options available on the list. These sub-options are displayed if you click on an option with an arrow.

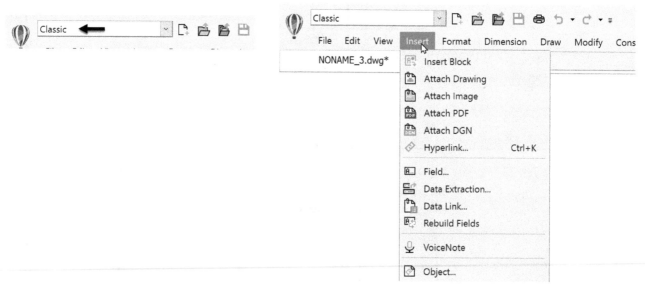

Changing the display of the Ribbon

You can change the presentation of the ribbon by clicking the arrow button located at the top of it. The ribbon can be displayed in three different modes, as shown below.

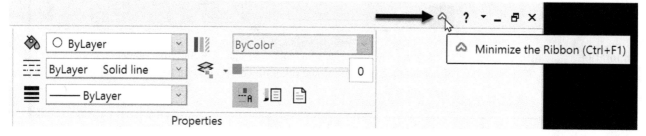

Minimized to Tabs

Home	Insert	Annotate	Sheet	Constraints	Manage	View	Plugins

Dialogs and Palettes

Dialogs and Palettes are part of the CorelCAD user interface. Using a dialog or a palette, you can easily specify many settings and options at a time. Examples of dialogs and palettes are as shown below.

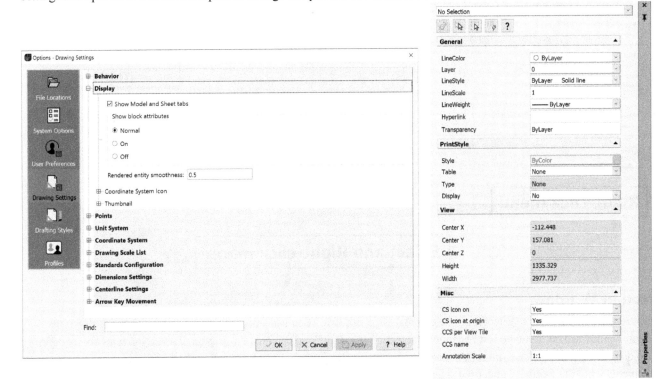

Shortcut Menus

Shortcut Menus appear when you right-click in the graphics window. CorelCAD provides various shortcut menus to help you access tools and options very easily and quickly. There are multiple types of shortcut menus available in CorelCAD. Some of them are discussed next.

Right-click Menu

This shortcut menu appears whenever you right-click in the graphics window without activating any command or selecting an object.

Select and Right-click menu

This shortcut menu appears when you select an object from the graphics window and right-click. It consists of editing and selection options.

Command Mode shortcut menu

This shortcut menu appears when you activate a command and right-click. It shows options depending upon the active command. The shortcut menu below shows the options related to the **Line** command.

Right-click menu

Select and Right-click menu

Command Mode Shortcut menu

Selection Window

A selection window is used to select multiple elements of a drawing. You can select various elements by using two types of selection windows. The first type is a rectangular selection window. You can create this type of selection window by defining its two diagonal corners. When you set the first corner of the selection window on the left and second corner on the right side, the elements which fall entirely under the selection window will be selected.

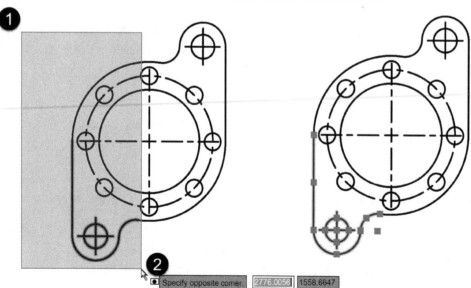

However, if you define the first corner on the right side and the second corner on the left side, the elements, which fall entirely or partially under the selection window, will be selected.

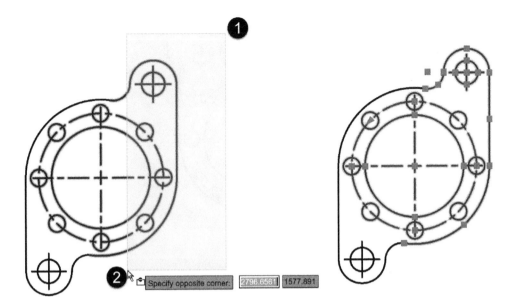

The second type of selection window is Lasso. Lasso is an irregular shape created by holding the left mouse button and dragging the pointer across the elements to select. If you drag the pointer from left to right, the elements falling entirely under the lasso will be selected.

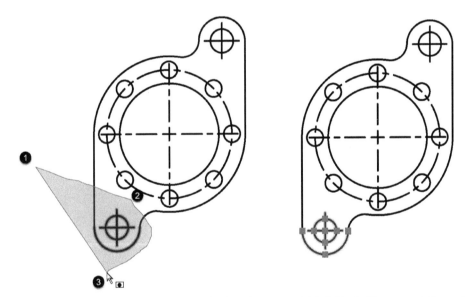

If you drag the pointer from right to left, the elements which fall wholly or partially under the lasso will be selected.

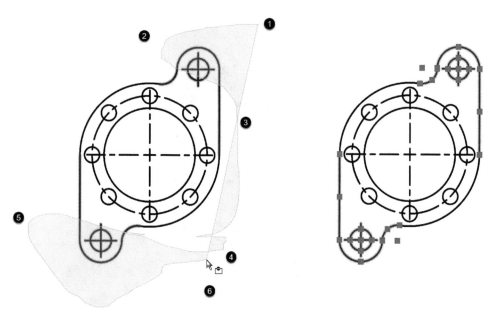

Help

Press F1 or click the Help icon located at the top right corner of the window to get help for any topic.

Tutorial 1: Creating the Floor Plan

In this example, you will learn to create an architectural drawing.

Creating Outer Walls

- Double-click on the **CorelCAD** icon on your desktop.

- Set the **Workspace** to **Drafting and Annotation**.

- Type **UNITSYSTEM** in the command window and press Enter.

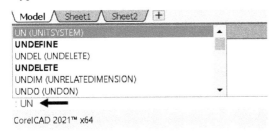

- On the **Unit System** page, select **Type > Architectural** from the **Length** section. Next, select **Precision > 0-01/16**.

- Select **Inches** from the **Block units format** drop-down in the **Unit Scale** section. Next, click **OK**.

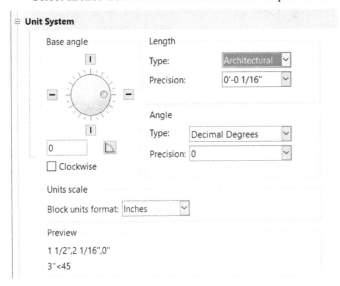

- Type **DRAWINGBOUNDS** in the command window and press Enter.

- Press Enter to accept 0, 0 as the lower limit.

- Type 100', 80' in the command window, and press Enter. The program sets the upper limit of the drawing.

- Make sure that the **Grid** icon is turned OFF on the status bar.

- On the ribbon, click **View > Navigate > Zoom Extents** drop-down > **Zoom Bounds**.
- On the Status bar, turn ON the **Ortho** icon.

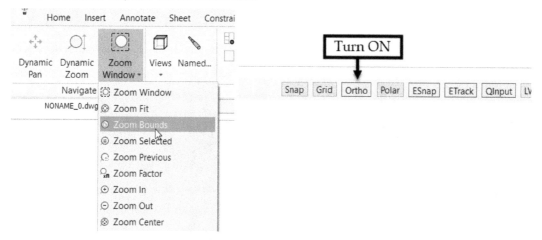

- On the Status bar, make sure that the **QInput** icon is turned ON.

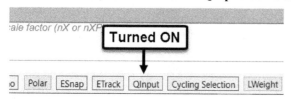

- On the ribbon, click **Home > Draw > Line**, and then select an arbitrary point. It defines the start point of the line.
- Move the pointer toward right horizontally and type-in 412 — press Enter.

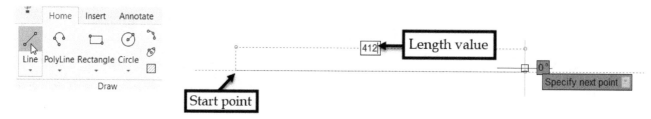

- Move the pointer vertically and type-in 338 — press Enter.
- Move the pointer onto the starting point of the drawing, and then move it upwards. You will notice that a dotted line appears.

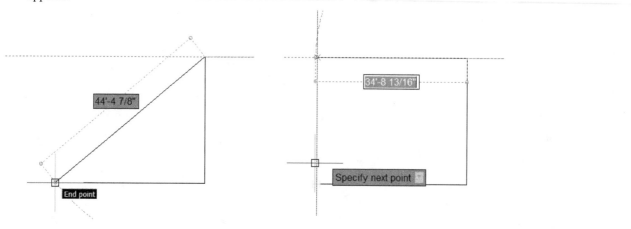

- Click to create a horizontal line. You will notice that the two horizontal lines are of the same length.
- Click the right mouse button and select **Close**.

- On the ribbon, click **Home > Modify > Offset**. Next, type-in 6 in the command window and press Enter.

- Select the left vertical line of the drawing.
- Move the pointer inside the drawing and click to create an offset line.
- Likewise, offset the other lines, as shown below.

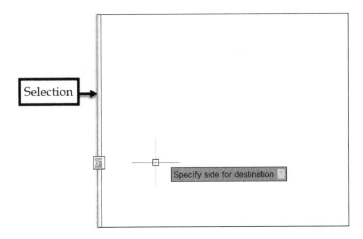

- On the **View** tab of the ribbon, click **Navigate** panel > **Zoom** drop-down > **Zoom Window**.
- Create a window on the top left corner of the drawing. The corner portion will be zoomed in.

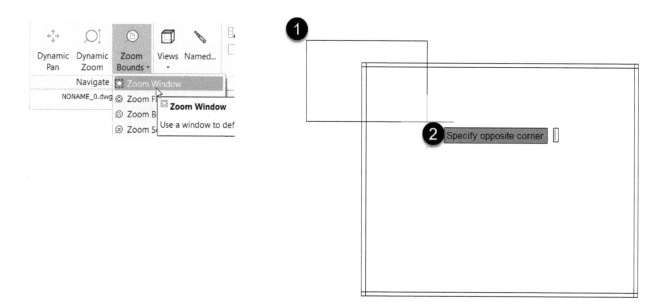

- On the ribbon, click **Home > Modify > Fillet**.

- Right-click and select the **Radius** option. Next, type in 0 — press Enter.

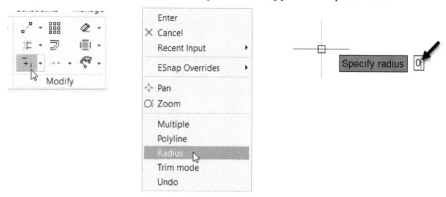

- Select the inner offset lines, as shown below.

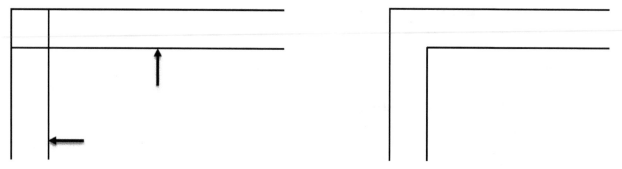

- On the **View** tab of the ribbon, click **Navigate** panel > **Zoom** drop-down > **Zoom Previous**. The drawing is displayed in the previous zoom scale.

- On the **View** tab of the ribbon, click **Navigate** panel > **Zoom** drop-down > **Zoom Window**.

- Create a window on the bottom left corner of the drawing.

- On the ribbon, click **Home > Modify > Fillet**.

- Select the inner offset lines, as shown below.

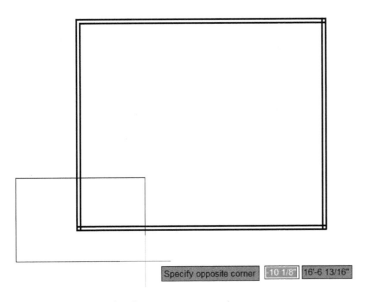

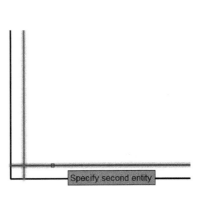

- Likewise, fillet the other inner corners, as shown.

- Click the **Save** icon on the **Quick Access Toolbar**. Type **Tutorial_1** in the **File name** box and click **Save**.
- Make sure that you save the drawing after each section.

Creating Inner Walls

- On the ribbon, click **Home > Modify > Offset** . Next, type-in **130** and press Enter.

- Select the inner line of the right sidewall. Next, move the pointer toward the left and click.

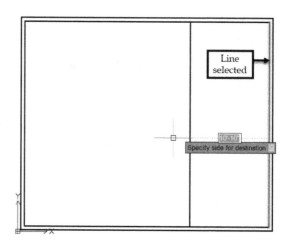

- Select the new offset line.
- Click the **Home** tab > **Modify** panel > **Copy** on the ribbon.
- Select the endpoint of the selected line as a base point.
- Move the pointer toward the left and type in 4, and then press Enter. A new line is created, and another line is attached to the pointer.

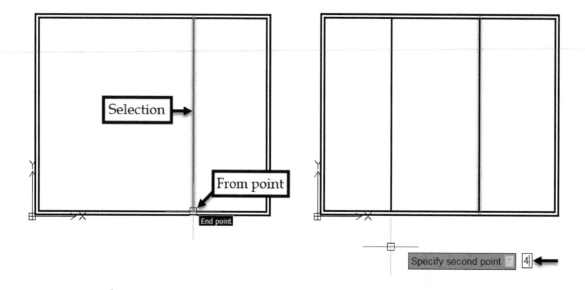

- Move the pointer toward the left and type in 118, and then press Enter.
- Move the pointer toward the left and type in 122, and then press Enter.
- Press Esc to come out of the **Copy** command.

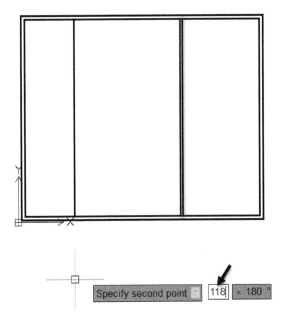 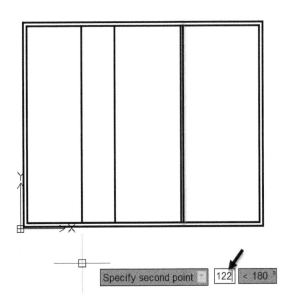

- Likewise, create horizontal offset lines, as shown below.

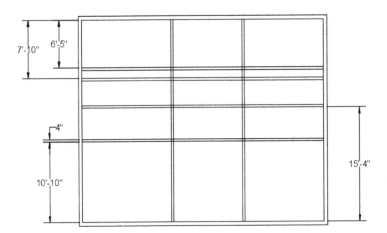

- On the ribbon, click **Home > Modify > Trim/Extend** drop-down > **Trim**.
- Press ENTER to select all entities as cutting edges. Next, click on the lines at the locations shown below.

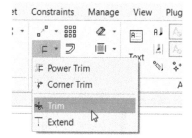

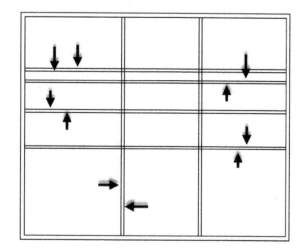

- Click **Home** tab > **Modify** panel > **Trim/Extend** drop-down > **Power Trim** on the ribbon.

- Press and hold the left mouse button and drag it across the horizontal lines, as shown below.

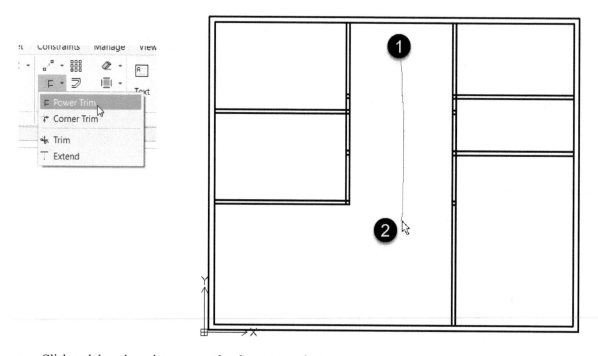

- Click and drag the pointer across the elements, as shown.

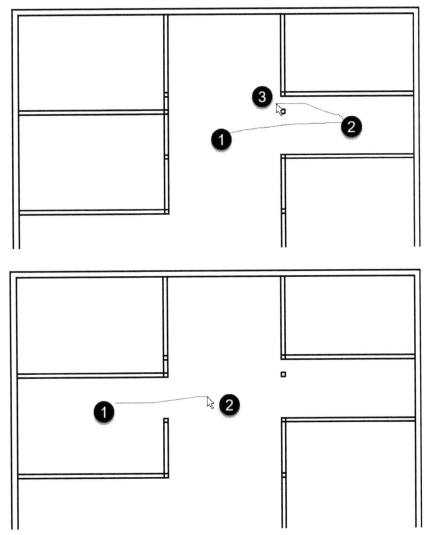

- Zoom to the top portion of the drawing by placing the pointer in the top portion and rotating the mouse scroll in the forward direction.

- On the ribbon, click **Home** tab > **Modify** panel > **Trim/Extend** drop-down > **Trim** ✄ .

- Press ENTER to select all the elements as cutting edges.

- Select the portion of the horizontal line that lies between the lines of the inner wall. The selected portions will be trimmed.

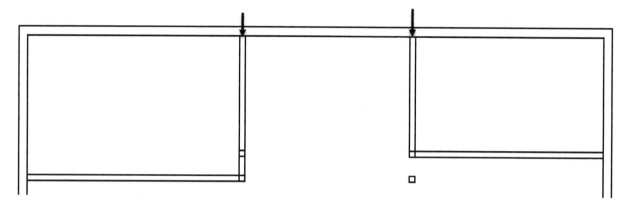

- Press and hold the mouse scroll wheel and drag downwards until the lower portion of the drawing is visible.
- Trim the unwanted portion, as shown below.

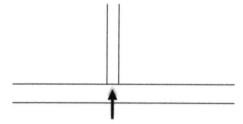

- Trim the unwanted portions, as shown below. Also, trim the unwanted portions at the corners.

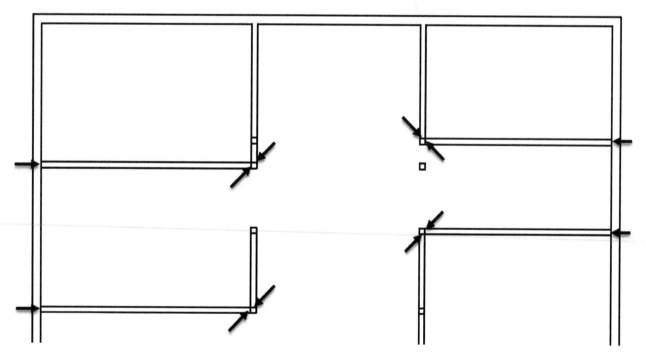

- Right-click and select **eRase** from the shortcut menu.
- Select the unwanted elements by dragging a selection window across them, as shown. Next, press ENTER.

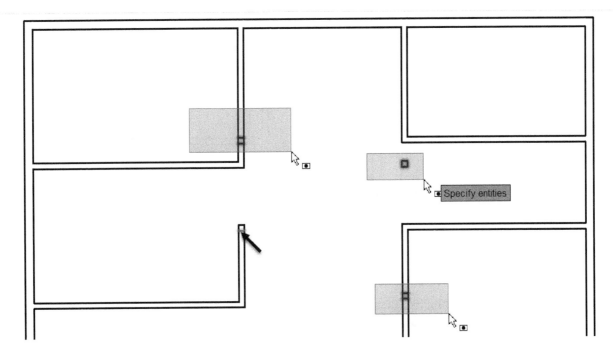

Creating Openings and Doors

- Activate the **Line** command and select the corner of the inner wall, as shown below.

- Move the pointer downward and select the other corner point.

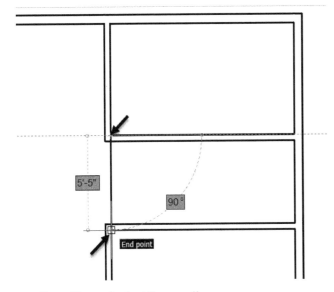

- Press Esc and select the new line.

- Select the middle point of the new line and move the pointer toward the right.

- Type-in 6 and press Enter.

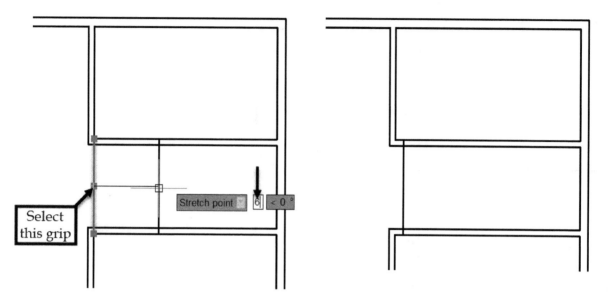

- On the ribbon, click **Home** tab > **Modify** panel > **Offset**. Type 32 as the offset distance, and then press ENTER.
- Select the new line and move rightwards, and then click.

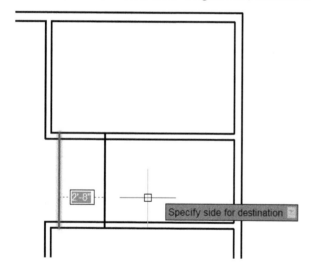

- On the ribbon, click **Home** tab > **Modify** panel > **Trim/Extend** drop-down > **Power Trim**.
- Click and drag the left mouse button across the unwanted portions, as shown.

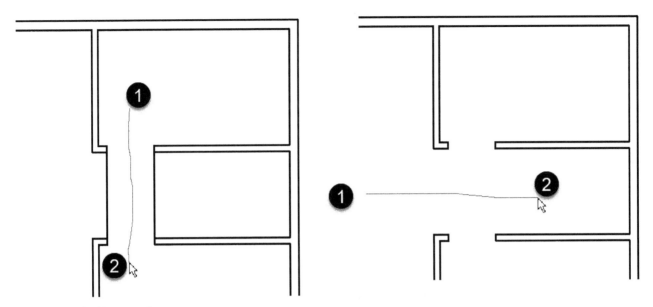

- Create the lines, as shown.
- Offset the newly created lines. The offset distances are given in the figure below.

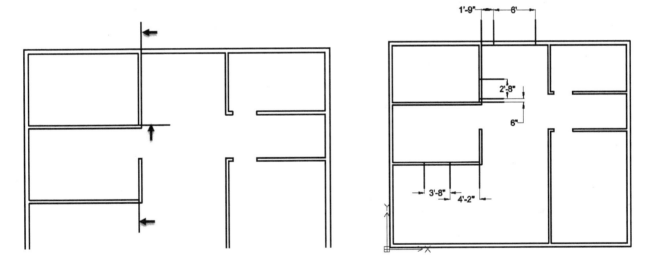

- On the ribbon, click **Home** tab > **Modify** panel > **Trim/Extend** drop-down > **Power Trim**.
- Click and pointer across the elements, as shown. Next, press ENTER.

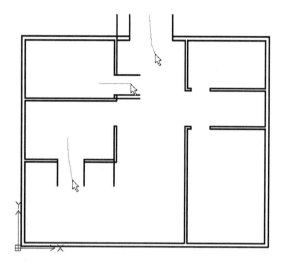 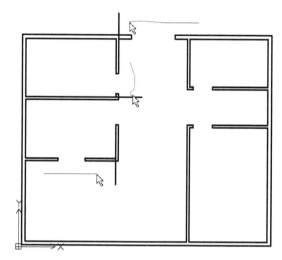

- Select the remaining unwanted lines and press DELETE.

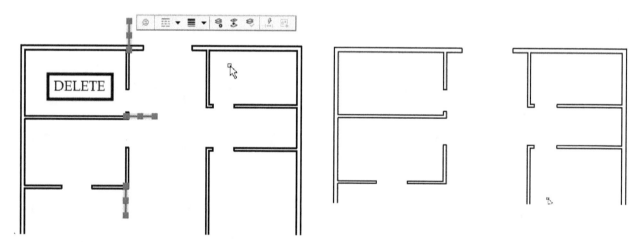

- On the ribbon, click **Home > Draw > Rectangle**. Next, select the endpoint of the opening, as shown below.

- Right click and select **Dimensions** from the shortcut menu.

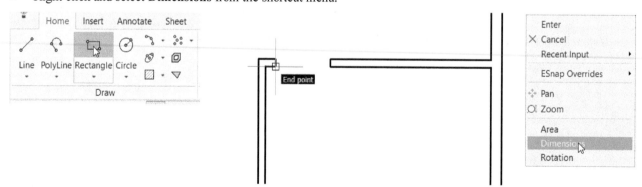

- Type-in 1 and press Enter. It defines the length of the rectangle.

- Type-in -32 and press Enter. It defines the width of the rectangle.

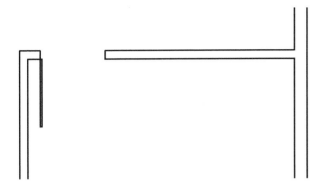

Now, you need to create the door swing.

- On the ribbon, click **Home > Draw > Arc** drop-down **> Start Center End**.

- Select the start, center, and end of the arc in the sequence shown below.

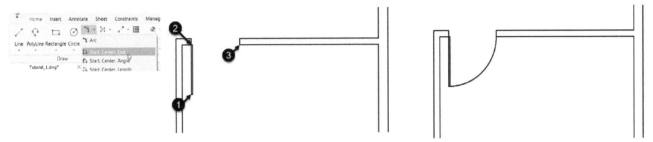

- Select the door and door swing. On the ribbon, click **Home > Modify > Copy**.

- Select the corner point of the rectangle as the base point.

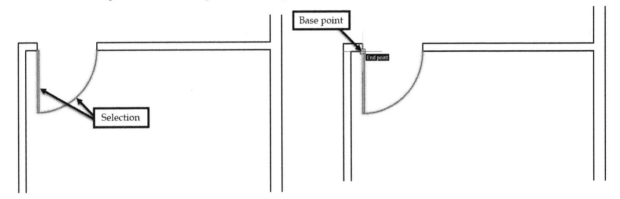

- Select the corner points of openings, as shown below.

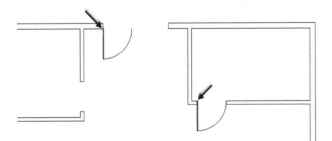

- Press Esc to deactivate the **Copy** command.

- Click the right mouse button on the **ESnap** icon on the status bar. Next, select **Settings** from the menu.

- Make sure that the **Midpoint** option is selected. Next, click **OK**.

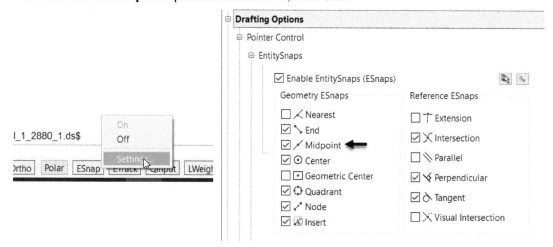

- On the ribbon, click **Home > Modify > Copy** drop-down > **Mirror**, and then select the door and swing of the bathroom, as shown. Press Enter to accept the selection.

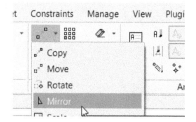

- Define the mirror line by selecting the points, as shown below.

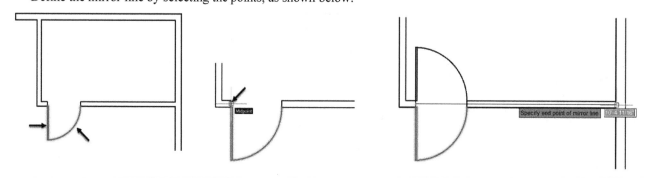

- Select **Yes** to delete the original object.

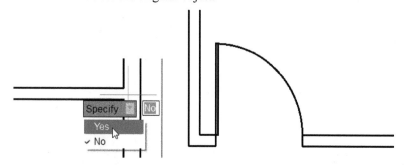

- On the ribbon, click **Home > Modify > Copy** drop-down > **Scale**, and then select the door & swing at the main entrance — press Enter.

- Select the base point, as shown below.

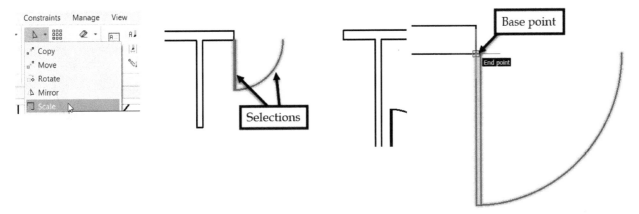

- Right click and select the **Reference** option from the shortcut menu.
- Select the two endpoints, as shown below. It defines the reference length of the objects. Now, you need to define the length up to which you want to scale the objects.
- Type-in 36 and press Enter. The objects will be scaled.

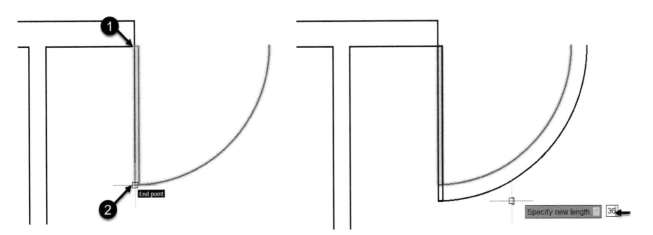

- Activate the **Mirror** command and select the door & swing at the entrance. Press Enter to accept the selection.
- Define the mirror line by selecting the points, as shown below.
- Select **No** to keep the original object.

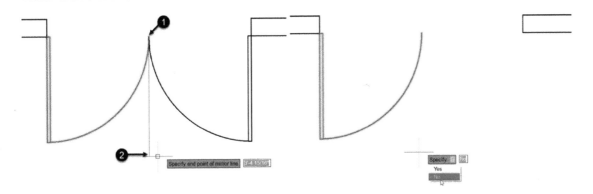

- Copy the door & swing of the bathroom and place it at the opening, as shown below.
- Press Esc.

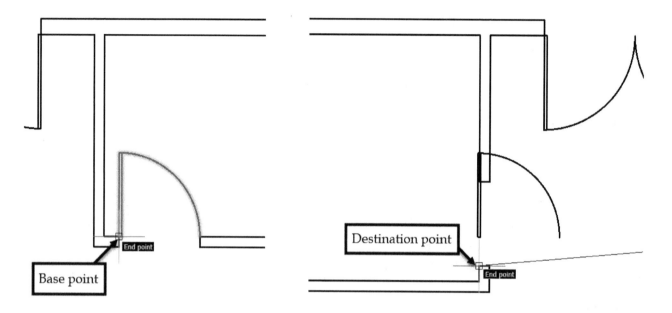

- On the ribbon, click **Home > Modify > Copy** drop-down > **Rotate**, and then select the copied object. Next, press Enter.
- Select the base point, as shown. Next, move the pointer vertically upward, and then click.

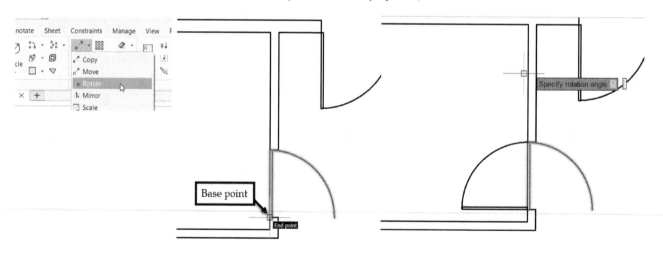

- Create an opening on the rear side of the plan, as shown below.

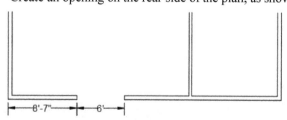

Now, you will create a sliding door in the opening.

- Activate the **Rectangle** command and select the corner point of the opening, as shown below.

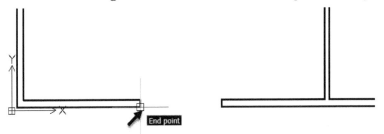

- Right click and select the **Dimensions** option.
- Specify 37 and 2 as the length and width of the rectangle, respectively.
- Move the pointer upward and click to create the rectangle.

- Type **M** in the command window and press Enter. Select the rectangle, and then press Enter.
- Select its lower-left corner point to define the base point. Move the pointer upward and type-in 1 in the command window, and then press Enter.

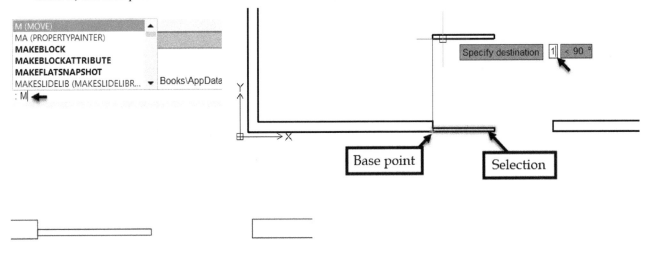

- On the ribbon, click **Home > Modify > Explode**, and select the rectangle. Press Enter to explode the rectangle.

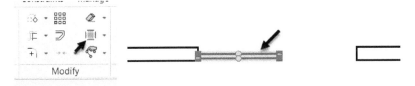

- Activate the **Offset** command and specify 2 as the offset distance.
- Offset the left and right vertical lines of the rectangle. Press **Esc** to deactivate the **Offset** command.

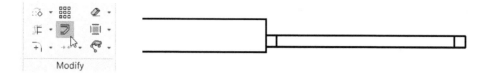

- Activate the **Line** command and select the midpoints of the offset lines. It creates a line connecting the offset lines. It creates one part of the sliding door.

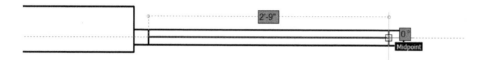

- Press **Esc** to deactivate the **Line** command.
- Type-in **CO** and press Enter. Next, drag a selection window covering all the elements of the sliding door. Press Enter.

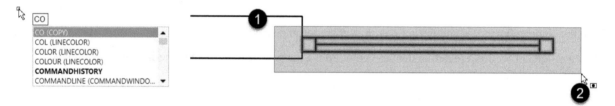

- Select the lower-left corner of the sliding door as the base point.
- Move the pointer and select the endpoint of the offset line, as shown.

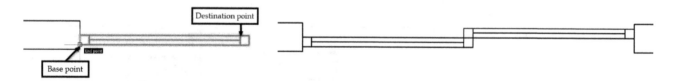

- Press **Esc** to deactivate the **Copy** command.

Now, you need to draw thresholds on the door openings.

- Zoom to the front door area using the **Zoom Window** tool.

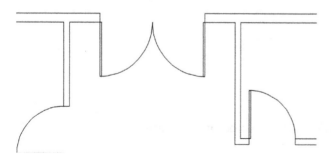

- Click the right mouse button on the **ESnap** icon on the status bar. Next, select **Settings** from the menu.

- Make sure that the **Nearest** option is selected. Next, click **OK**.

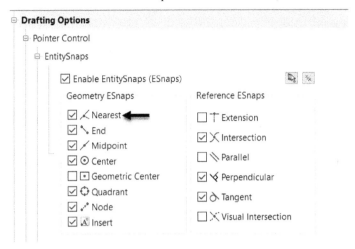

- Type-in **L** in the command window and press Enter.

- Press and hold the **Shift** key and click the right mouse button.

- Select **From** from the shortcut menu and click the endpoint of the door opening, as shown below.

- Move the point on the horizontal line. Next, press the TAB key and type in 3, and then press Enter. It defines the start point of the line at 3 distance from the endpoint.

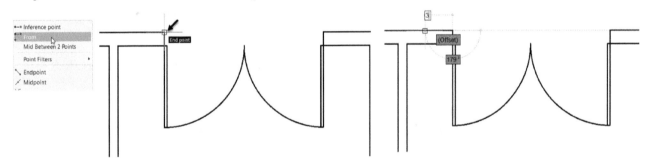

- Move the pointer up and type-in 2, and then press Enter.

- Move the pointer toward the right and type in 78, and then press Enter.

- Move the pointer downward and type in 2, and then press Enter. It creates a threshold.

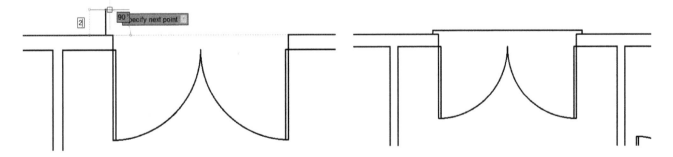

- Press Esc to deactivate the **Line** command.

- Likewise, create a threshold on the sliding glass door.

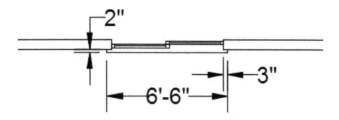

Creating Kitchen Fixtures

- Zoom to the kitchen area by using the **Zoom Window** tool.

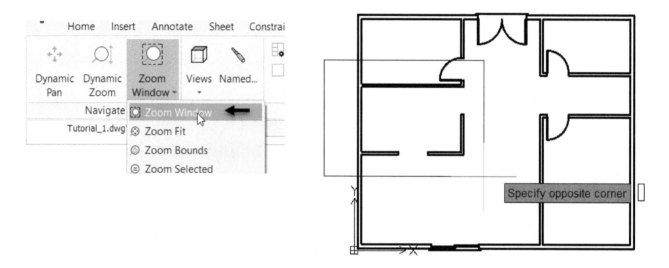

- Activate the **Offset** command and specify 26 as the offset distance. Next, offset the lines shown below.
- On the ribbon, click **Home** tab > **Modify** panel > **Trim/Extend** drop-down > **Corner Trim**.

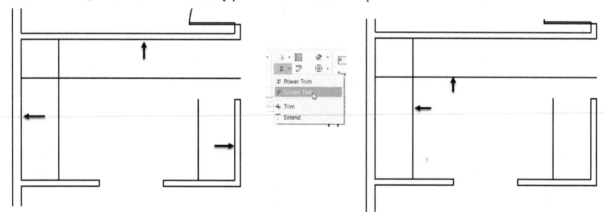

- Create another offset line at 54 distance, and then trim the unwanted elements.

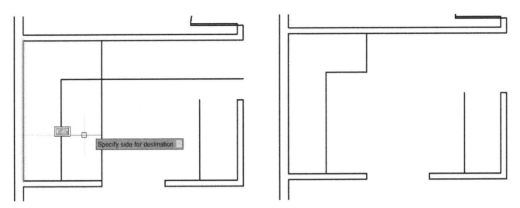

- Create another line, as shown below.

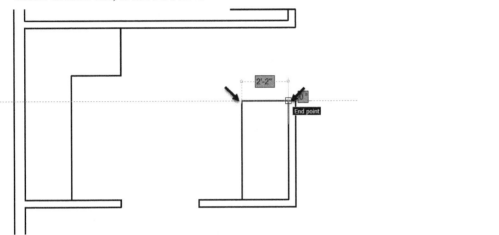

Now, you have finished drawing the counters. You need to draw a refrigerator, stove and sink.

- Type-in **REC** in the command window and press Enter. It activates the **Rectangle** command.

- Select the corner point of the counter. Next, right-click and select the **Dimensions** option.

- Type **28** and press ENTER to define the horizontal dimension.

- Type **-28** and press ENTER to define the vertical dimension.

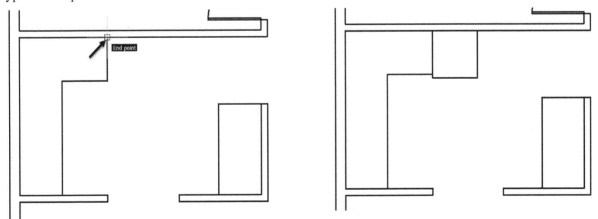

- Select the rectangle and click **Home** tab > **Modify** panel > **Copy** drop-down > **Move**.

- Select the top left corner of the rectangle. Next, move the pointer toward right and type 2. Press ENTER to move the rectangle.

- Likewise, move the rectangle 2 inches and downwards.

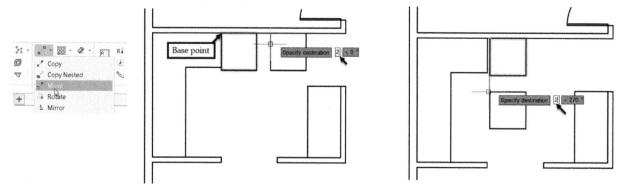

- Create the outline of the stove using the **Offset** and **Trim** commands.

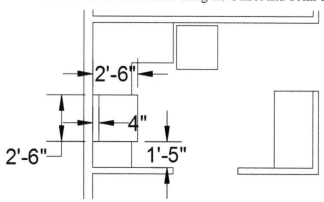

Now, you need to create the sink.

- Use the **Offset** command and create offset lines, as shown below.

- Trim the unwanted elements, as shown below.

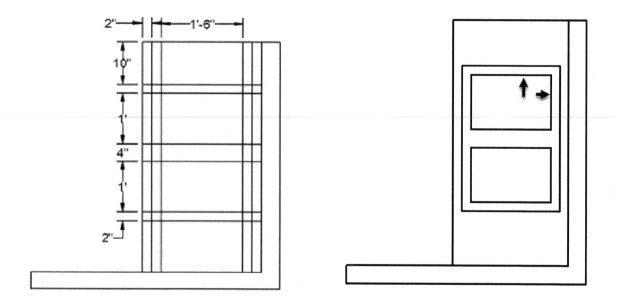

- On the ribbon, click **Home** tab > **Modify** panel > **Fillet**. Next, right click and select **Radius**.

- Type 2 and press ENTER. Next, select the horizontal and vertical lines forming a corner, as shown.

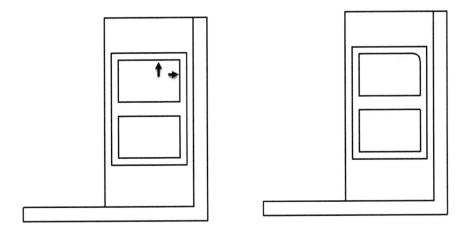

- Likewise, fillet the remaining corners with a fillet radius of 2 and 4, respectively.

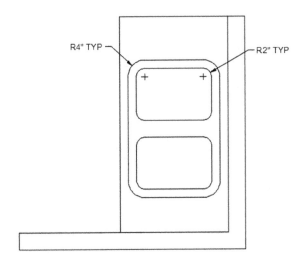

- On the ribbon, click **Home** tab > **Draw** panel > **Line** drop-down > **Infinite Line**.
- Right-click and select **Horizontal** from the shortcut menu. Next, select the midpoints of the vertical lines, as shown.

  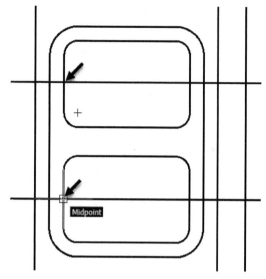

- Press ENTER twice to deactivate the **Infinite Line** command and then activate it again.

- Right click and select **Vertical** from the shortcut menu. Next, select the midpoint of the horizontal line, as shown.

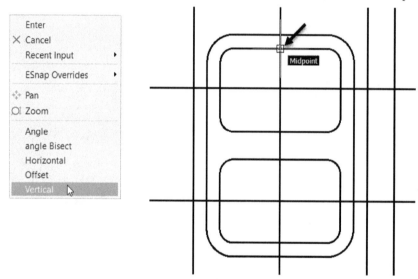

- On the ribbon, click **Home** tab > **Draw** panel > **Circle** drop-down > **Center, Diameter**.

- Select the intersection point of the two infinite lines, as shown.

- Move the pointer outward, and then type 4. Next, press ENTER.

- Press ENTER and select the intersection point of the infinite lines. Next, move the pointer outward, type 6, and press ENTER.

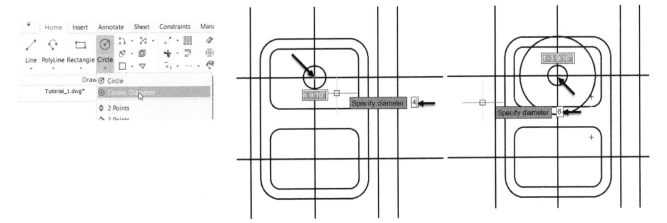

- Likewise, create two more circles, as shown.

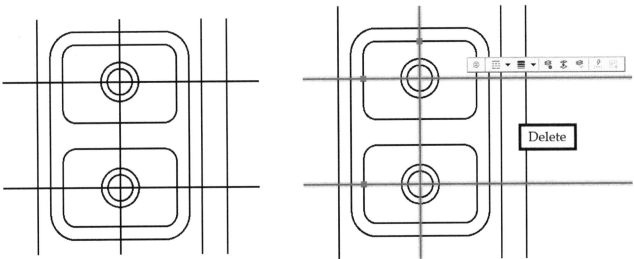

Delete

Creating Bathroom Fixtures

- Zoom into the bathroom area and create offset lines, as shown below.

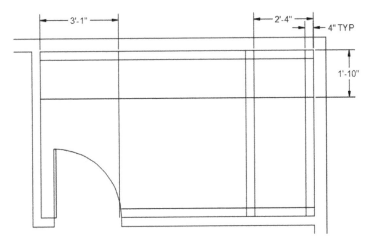

- Trim the unwanted elements, as shown below.
- Fillet the corners, as shown below. The fillet radius is 4.

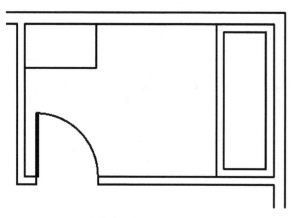
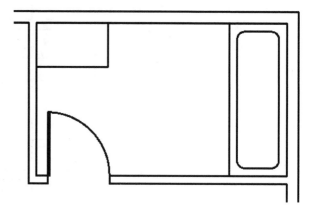

- Create two infinite lines, as shown.
- On the ribbon, click **Home > Draw > Ellipse drop-down > Center**.
- Select the intersection point of the infinite lines, as shown.
- Move the pointer toward the right and type in 10, and then press Enter. It defines the major radius of the ellipse.
- Move the pointer downward and type in 5, and then press Enter. It defines the minor radius of the ellipse.

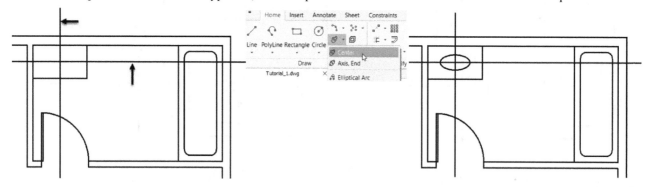

- Likewise, create another ellipse of 11 major radius and 7 minor radius.
- Delete the infinite lines.

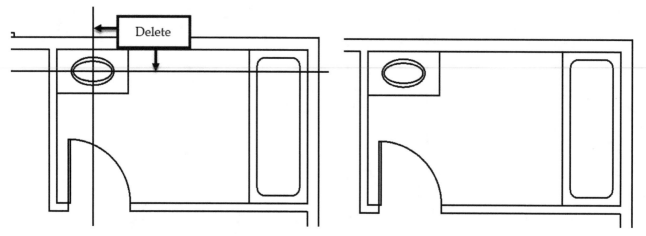

- Select the outer ellipse, and then click on its center point.
- Move the pointer up and type-in 1, and then press Enter. The outer ellipse moves up.

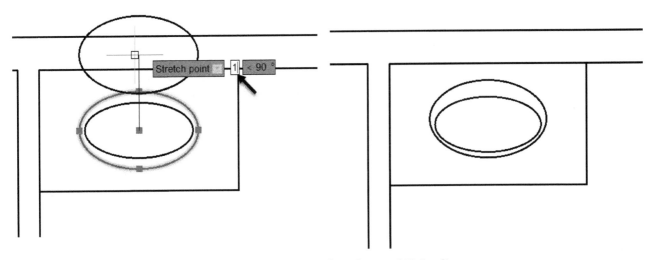

- On the ribbon, click **Home** > **Draw** panel > **Rectangle** drop-down > **3 Point Corner**.
- Select the top-right corner of the washbasin. Next, move the pointer vertically downward.
- Type 9 and press ENTER. Next, move the pointer horizontally toward the right.
- Type 22 and press ENTER.

- Move the rectangle up to 19.5 rightwards and 1 downwards.

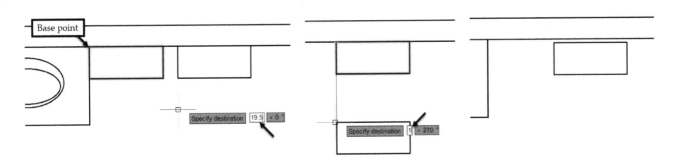

- On the ribbon, click **Home** > **Draw** > **Ellipse** drop-down > **Axes**.
- Select the midpoint of the lower horizontal line of the rectangle.
- Move the pointer downward and type in 18, and then press Enter. Type-in 6 as the minor radius and press Enter.

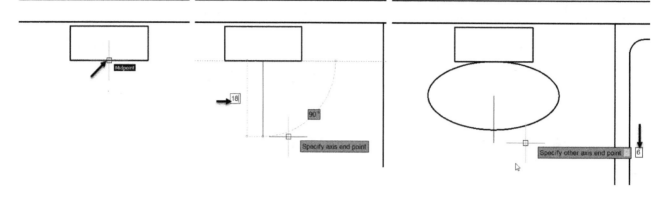

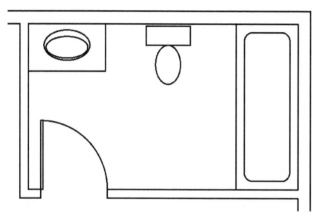

Adding Furniture using Blocks

- On the ribbon, click **Home** tab > **Draw** panel > **Rectangle** drop-down > **Corner**.

- Click in the empty space to specify the first corner of the rectangle.

- Right-click and select **Dimensions** from the shortcut menu.

- Type **72** as the horizontal dimension and press ENTER.

- Type **36** as the vertical dimension and press ENTER.

- On the ribbon, click **Home** tab > **Draw** panel > **Rectangle** drop-down > **3 Point Center**.

- Select the midpoint of the left vertical edge of the rectangle.

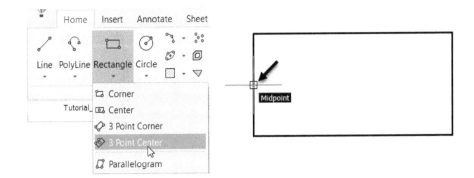

- Move the pointer toward left, type 9, and then press ENTER.
- Move the pointer downward, type 9, and then press ENTER.

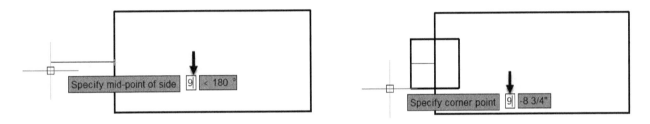

- Select the newly created rectangle and click **Home** tab > **Modify** panel > **Copy** drop-down > **Move**.
- Select the midpoint of the right vertical edge of the rectangle.
- Move the pointer toward the left, type 11, and press ENTER; the rectangle is moved.

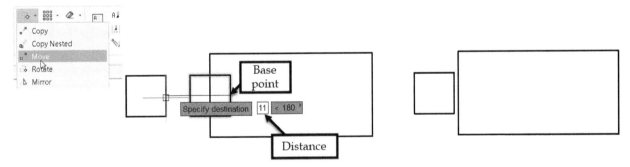

- On the ribbon, click **Home** tab > **Modify** panel > **Fillet** drop-down > **Chamfer**.
- Right-click and select **Distance** from the shortcut menu.
- Type 2 and press ENTER.
- Type 18 and press ENTER.
- Select the left vertical and horizontal bottom edges of the rectangle, as shown.
- Press ENTER to activate the **Chamfer** command.
- Select the left vertical and top horizontal edges of the rectangle.

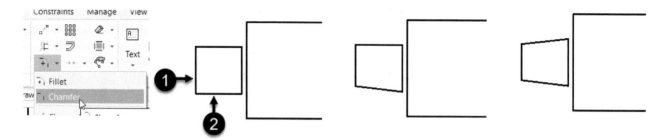

- Select the chamfered rectangle and click **Home** tab > **Modify** panel > **Copy** drop-down > **Mirror** on the ribbon.

- Select the midpoint of the lower horizontal edge of the large rectangle.

- Move the pointer vertically upward and click to define the mirror line. Next, select **No** to keep the original object.

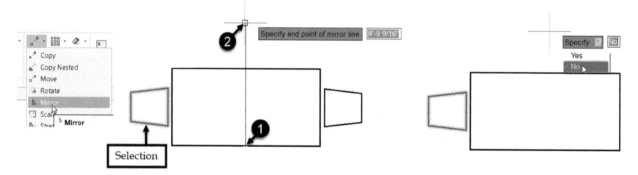

- Select the chamfered rectangle on the left side.

- Click **Home** tab > **Modify** panel > **Copy** drop-down > **Rotate** on the ribbon.

- Select the midpoint of the top horizontal edge of the large rectangle. Right click and select **Copy** from the menu.

- Move the pointer vertically upward and click.

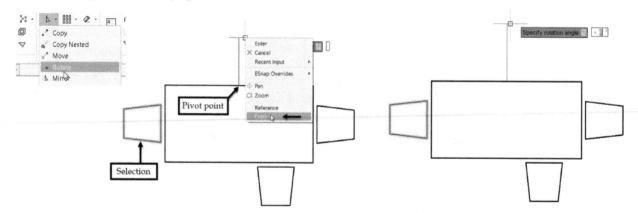

- Mirror the rotated rectangle, as shown.

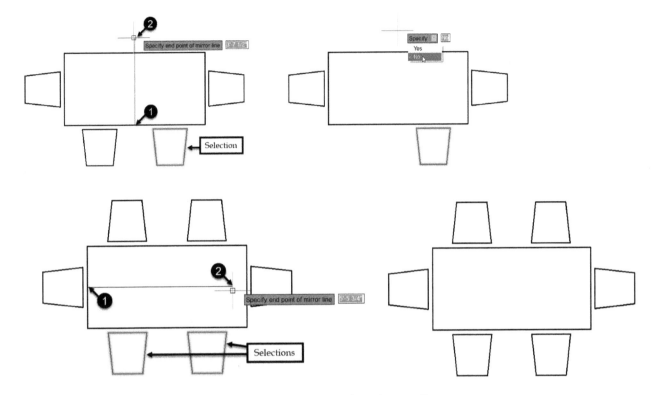

- On the ribbon, click **Home** tab > **Draw** panel > **Rectangle** drop-down > **Corner**.
- Click in the empty space. Next, right click and select **Dimensions**.
- Type 80 as the horizontal distance and press ENTER.
- Type 62 as the vertical distance and press ENTER.

- Press ENTER and select the midpoint of the right vertical edge of the rectangle. Next, right click and select **Dimensions**.
- Type -15 as the horizontal distance and press ENTER.
- Type 20 as the vertical distance and press ENTER.

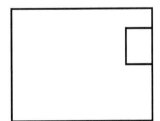

- Select the rectangle and click **Home > Modify > Copy** drop-down > **Move**.
- Select the lower right corner of rectangle.
- Move the pointer toward left and upwards by 2 inches, as shown.

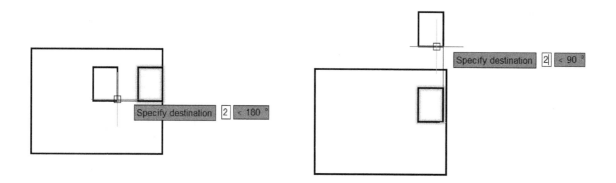

- Create a mirrored copy of the rectangle, as shown.

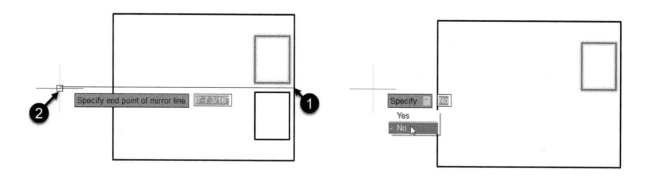

- Select the large rectangle of the bed and click **Home** tab > **Modify** panel > **Explode** on the ribbon.

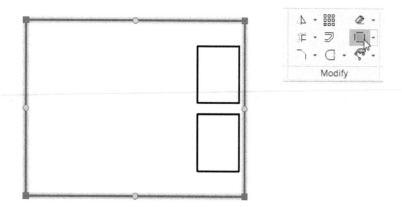

- Select the right vertical line of the exploded rectangle and click **Home** tab > **Modify** panel > **Offset**.
- Type **14** and press ENTER. Next, move the pointer toward the left and click.
- Press ENTER to activate the **Offset** command. Type **4** and press ENTER.
- Select the offset line and move the pointer toward the left. Next, click to create another offset line.

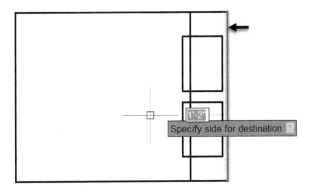 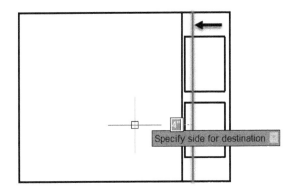

- Click **Home** > **Draw** > **Rectangle** drop-down > **Corner** on the ribbon.
- Select the lower endpoint of the first offset line. Next, right-click and select **Dimensions**.
- Type -15 and press ENTER to define the horizontal distance.
- Type 15 and press ENTER to define the vertical distance.

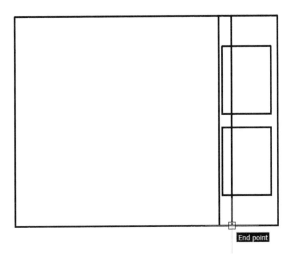 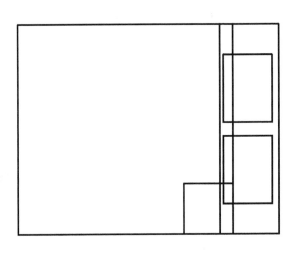

- On the ribbon, click **Home** > **Draw** > **Line**. Next, select the top-right and bottom-left corners of the rectangle.

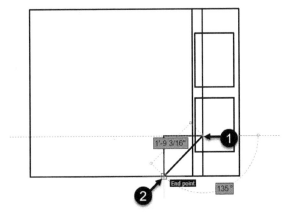

- On the ribbon, click **Home** > **Modify** > **Trim/Extend** drop-down > **Trim**. Next, press ENTER.
- Trim the unwanted portions of the rectangles and offset lines, as shown.

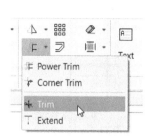

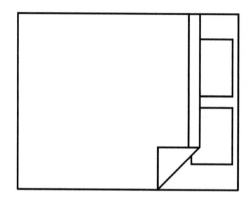

- On the ribbon, click **Insert** tab > **Block** panel > **Define**. Next, type **Dining Set** in the **Name** box on the **Block Definition** dialog.

- Click the **Select in graphics** area icon in the **Entities** section. Next, create a selection window across the dining set.

- Press ENTER and click the **Select in graphics area** icon in the **Base point** section.

- Select the lower-left corner of the rectangle, as shown.

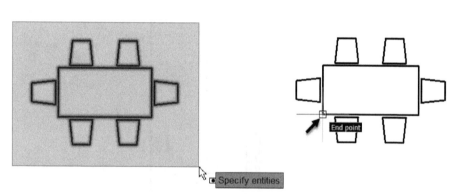

- Select the **Convert to Block** option and click **OK**.

- Select the Dining set block, and then click on the grip located at the bottom-left corner.

- Move the block and place it at the location shown below.

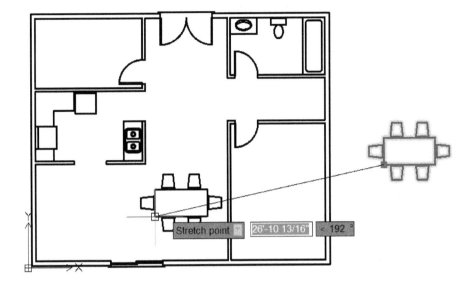

- On the ribbon, click **Insert** tab > **Block** panel > **Define**. Next, type **Bed** in the **Name** box on the **Block Definition** dialog.

- Click the **Select in graphics** area icon in the **Entities** section. Next, create a selection window across the bed.

- Press ENTER and click the **Select in graphics area** icon in the **Base point** section.

- Select the lower-left corner of the rectangle, as shown.

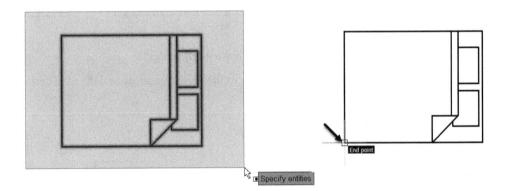

- Select the **Convert to Block** option and click **OK**.

- Activate the **Rectangle** command and select the corner point of the bedroom, as shown.

- Right click and select the **Dimensions** option from the shortcut menu. Next, specify -86 and -27.5 as the horizontal and vertical dimensions of the rectangle, respectively.

- Move the pointer downward and click create the rectangle.

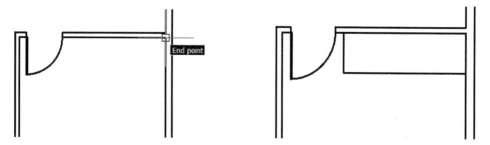

- Create another rectangle by selecting the corner points, as shown below.

- Offset the rectangle by a distance of 47.5 inwards. Next, delete the original rectangle.

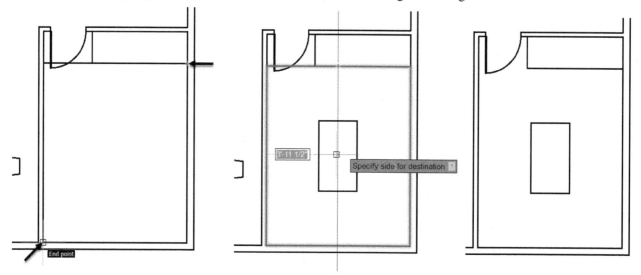

- Select the bed and click on the grip located at the bottom left corner.

- Move the pointer and select the bottom left corner of the offset rectangle to define the destination point.

- Delete the offset rectangle.

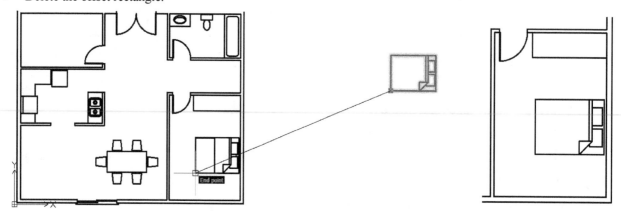

Adding Windows

- In the empty space, create the window using the **Line** command, as shown below.

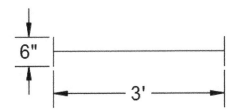

- On the ribbon, click **Insert > Block > Define**.
- On the **Block Definition** dialog, type-in **Window** in the **Name** box.
- Click the **Select in graphics** area icon in the **Entities** section. Next, create a selection window across all the newly created elements.
- Press ENTER and click the **Select in graphics area** icon in the **Base point** section.
- Select the lower-left corner of the window.

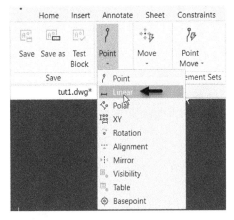

- On the dialog, check the **Edit in block editor** option and click **OK**. It creates the block and opens it in the **Block Editor**.
- On the **Edit Block** ribbon, click **Elements > Point drop-down > Linear**.
- Click the endpoints of the horizontal line.
- Move the pointer downward and click to define the parameter location.

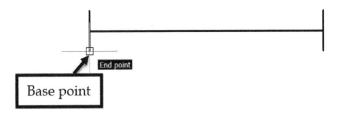

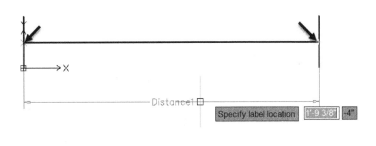

- Select 2 to specify the number of grips to be displayed when you select the parameter.

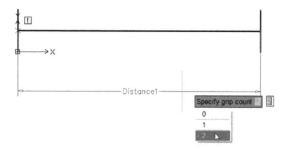

- Click the **Move** drop-down > **Stretch** 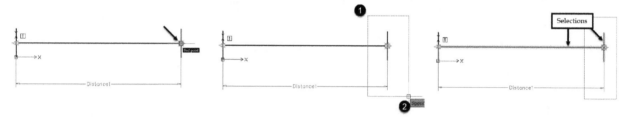 on the **Activities** panel. Next, select the **Distance1** parameter.

- Select the right endpoint of the horizontal line. It defines the point that can be used to stretch the block.

- Create a window around the selected endpoint.

- Select the horizontal and right vertical lines, and then press Enter. It defines the elements that can be stretched.

- Click the **Test Block** icon on the **Save** panel of the **Edit Block** ribbon. The **Test Block Window** appears.

- Select the block and click the arrow grip. Drag the pointer to stretch the block.

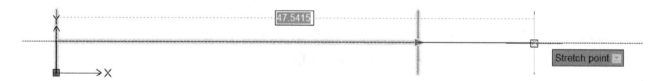

- Close the **Test Block Window** tab.

- Click the **Save** icon on the **Save** panel of the **Edit Block** tab of the ribbon.

- Click the **Close** icon on the **Close** panel of the **Edit Block** tab of the ribbon. It closes the **Block Editor** window. Now, you need to place the windows.

- On the ribbon, click **Home** > **Draw** > **Line** drop-down > **Infinite Line** .

- Right click and select **Offset**. Next, type 95, and press ENTER.

- Select the right vertical line, as shown. Next, move the pointer toward the left and click.

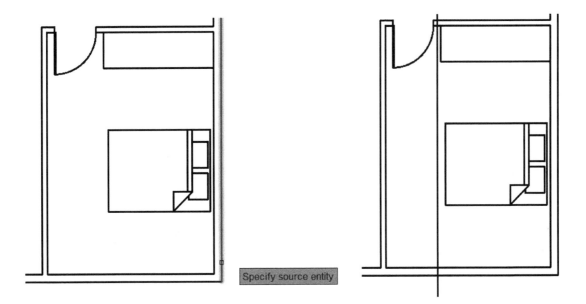

Specify source entity

- Press ENTER twice. Next, right click and select **Offset** from the shortcut menu.
- Type 26 and press ENTER. Next, select the horizontal line of the kitchen wall, as shown.
- Move the pointer upward and click.

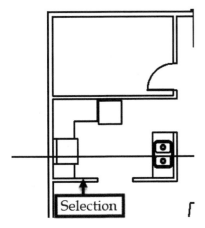

Selection

- Press ENTER twice. Next, right click and select **Offset** from the shortcut menu.
- Type 29 and press ENTER. Next, select the horizontal line, as shown.
- Move the pointer upward and click.

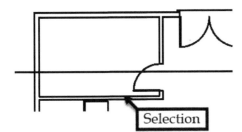

Selection

- Press ENTER twice. Next, right click and select **Offset** from the shortcut menu.

- Type 16 and press ENTER. Next, select the horizontal line, as shown.
- Move the pointer upward and click.
- Press ENTER twice. Next, right click and select **Offset** from the shortcut menu.
- Type 54 and press ENTER. Next, select the vertical line, as shown.
- Move the pointer toward the right and click.

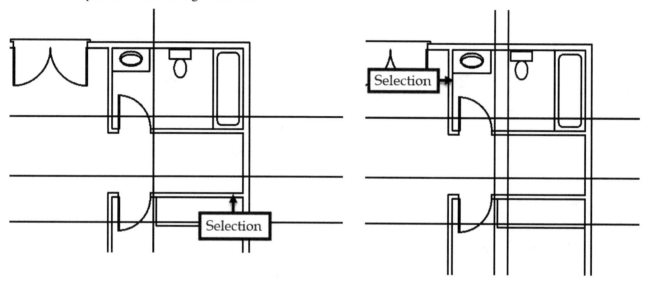

- On the ribbon, click **Insert > Block > Insert**. Next, select **Window** from the **Name** drop-down.
- Check the **Specify Later** option from the **Position** section. Next, click **OK**.

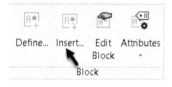

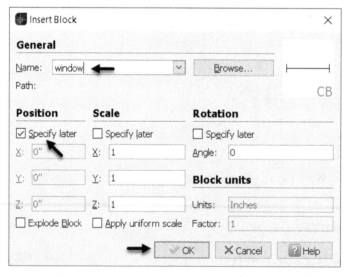

- Select the intersection point between the infinite line and the horizontal line, as shown. The **Window** block will be placed at the specified location.
- Select the **Window** block and drag the arrow grip.
- Type-in **54** and press Enter. It changes the window size to 54.

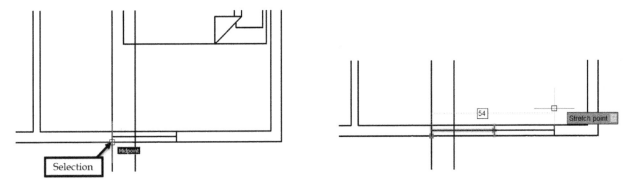

- Press ENTER and select **Window** from the **Name** drop-down.

- Select the intersection point between the infinite line and the horizontal line, as shown.

- Change the window size to 26.

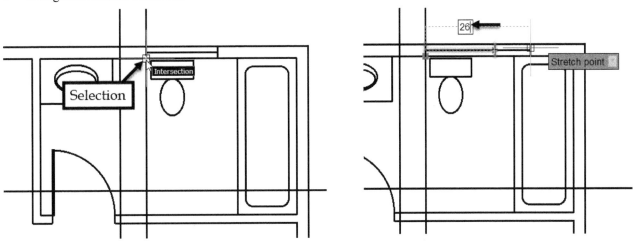

- On the ribbon, click **Insert > Block > Insert**. Next, select **Window** from the **Name** drop-down.

- Type-in **90 Angle** box and click **OK**.

- Place the **Window** block on the kitchen wall, as shown below.

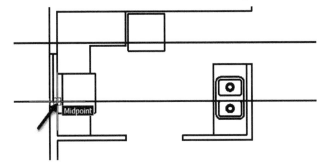

- Likewise, place the window blocks, as shown below. Next, delete the infinite lines.

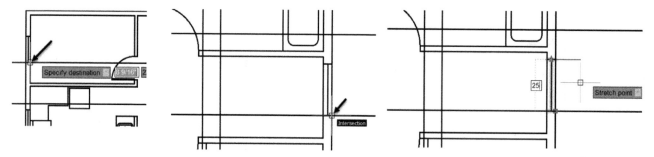

Arranging Objects of the drawing in Layers

- On the ribbon, click the **Home > Layers > Layers Manager**. It displays the Layer Manager.

- On the **Layers Manager** palette, click the **New** button.

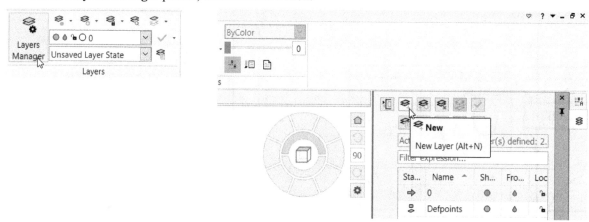

- Type **Wall** in the layer **Name** box and press Enter.

- Create another layer, and then type-in **Door** — press Enter.

- Likewise, create other layers, as shown below.

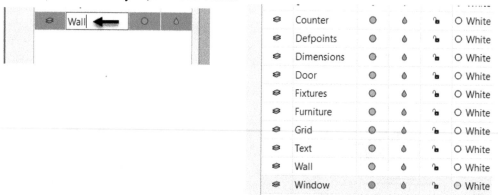

	Name				
🅢	Counter	◎	◊	🔒	○ White
🅢	Defpoints	◎	◊	🔒	○ White
🅢	Dimensions	◎	◊	🔒	○ White
🅢	Door	◎	◊	🔒	○ White
🅢	Fixtures	◎	◊	🔒	○ White
🅢	Furniture	◎	◊	🔒	○ White
🅢	Grid	◎	◊	🔒	○ White
🅢	Text	◎	◊	🔒	○ White
🅢	Wall	◎	◊	🔒	○ White
🅢	Window	◎	◊	🔒	○ White

- Click the **Line Color** drop-down of the **Counter** layer, and then select **Red**.

- Click the **Line Color** drop-down of the **Dimensions** layer, and then select the **Specify Color** option.
- Select the **Index color 8** from the **Line Color** dialog. Next, click **OK**.

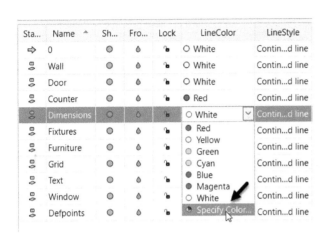 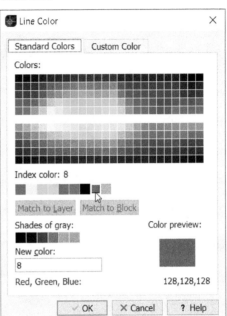

- Likewise, change the line colors of the remaining layers, as shown.

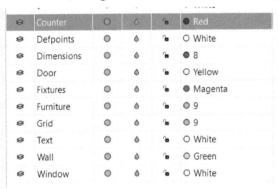

- Click the **LineStyle** drop-down of the **Grid** layer, and then select **Other**.
- Click the **Load** icon on the **Line Style** dialog. Next, select the DASHED line style from the **Load LineStyles** dialog, and then click **OK**.

 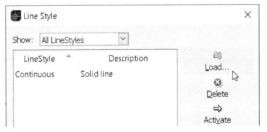

- Select the DASHED line style from the **Line Style** dialog, and then click **OK**.

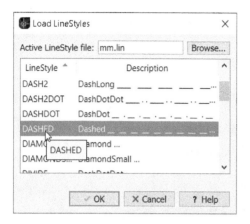
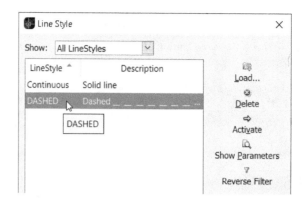

- Click the **LineWeight** drop-down of the **Counter** layer and select 0.35 mm.

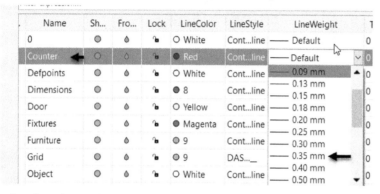

- Likewise, change the Lineweights of the remaining layers, as shown.

- Close the **Layer Manager palette**.

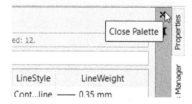

- Select the Dining set, cupboard, and bed.

- On the ribbon, click **Home > Layers > Layer Manager drop-down > Furniture**. The selected objects will be transferred to the **Furniture** layer.

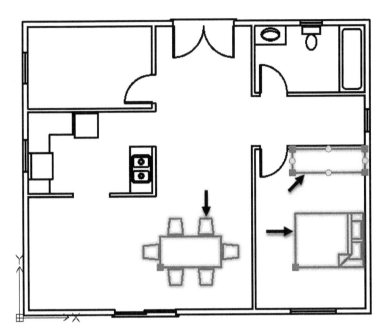
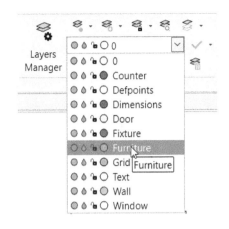

- Press Esc to deselect the selected objects.

- Select the kitchen and bathroom fixtures and click **Home** > **Layers** > **Layer Manager** drop-down > **Fixtures.**

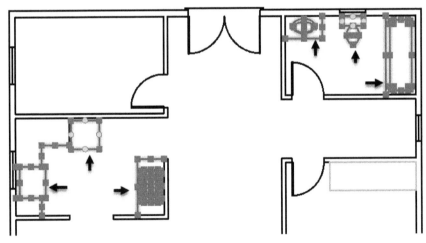

- Press Esc.

- Likewise, transfer the remaining objects onto their respective layers, as shown.

- Open the **Layers Manager** and click the green dots associated with Door, Window, Fixtures, Furniture, and Counter layers. It will hide the corresponding layers.

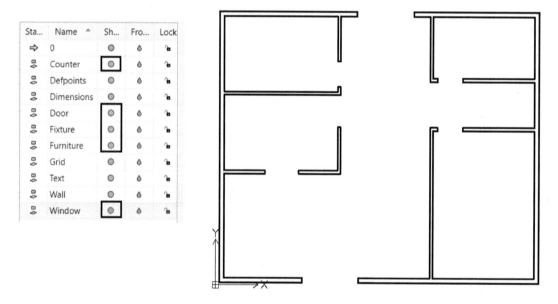

Sta...	Name ▲	Sh...	Fro...	Lock
⇨	0	◎	◊	🔓
☰	Counter	◉	◊	🔓
☰	Defpoints	◎	◊	🔓
☰	Dimensions	◎	◊	🔓
☰	Door	◉	◊	🔓
☰	Fixture	◎	◊	🔓
☰	Furniture	◉	◊	🔓
☰	Grid	◎	◊	🔓
☰	Text	◎	◊	🔓
☰	Wall	◎	◊	🔓
☰	Window	◉	◊	🔓

- Create a selection window and select all the walls.
- On the ribbon, click **Home > Layers > Layer Manager drop-down > Wall**. All the walls will be transferred to the **Wall** layer.

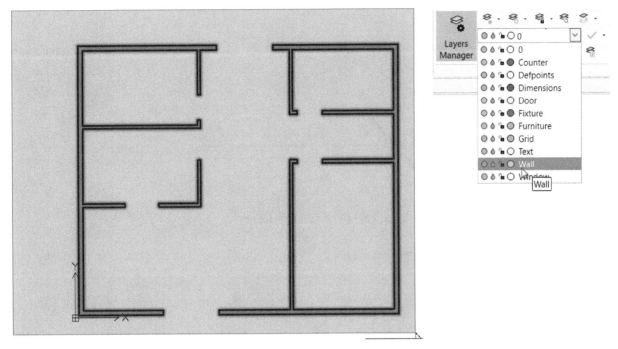

- Now, turn ON the hidden layers by clicking the bulb symbols.

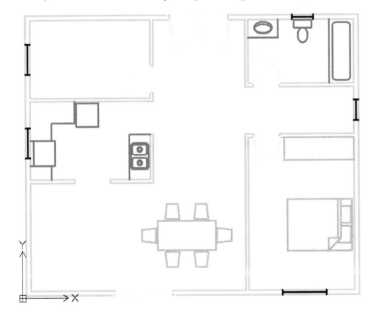

Creating Grid Lines

- On the ribbon, click **Home > Layers > Layer Manager** drop-down > **Grid**. The Grid layer becomes active.
- Activate the **Line** command. Press and hold the Shift key and right-click, and then select the **Mid Between 2 Points** option.
- Select the endpoints of the wall, as shown below.

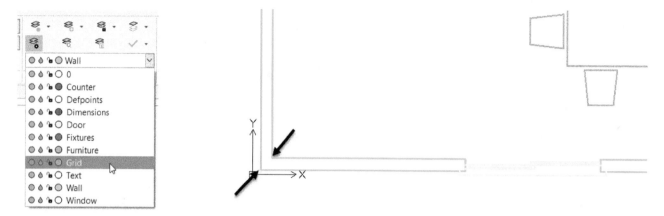

- Move the point upward and click to draw a vertical line of arbitrary length.

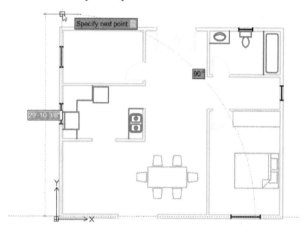

- Press Esc to deactivate the **Line** command. Next, select the line to display grips on it.

- Click the lower end grip and drag the pointer to increase the length of the line.

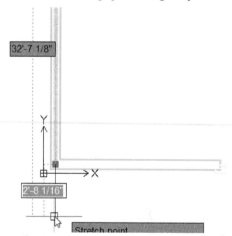

- Activate the **Offset** command and offset the grid line up to 406.

- Create other grid lines, as shown below.

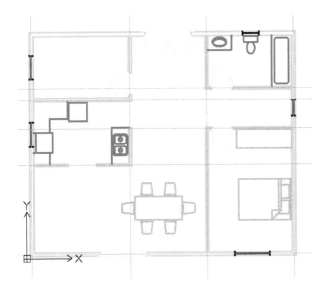

- Create a new layer called **Grid Bubble** and make it current.

- Create a circle of 12 diameter in the empty space.

- On the ribbon, click **Insert > Block Definition > Define Block Attributes**.

- On the **Block Attribute Definition** dialog, type-in GRIDBUBBLE in the **Name** box and select **Justification > Middle center**.

- Type-in 6″ in the **Height** box and click **OK**.

- Select the center point of the circle. The attribute text will be placed at its center.

- On the ribbon, click **Insert > Block > Define**.
- Type-in **Grid bubble** in the **Name** box and click the **Select in graphics area** button under the **Entities** section.
- Draw a crossing window to select the circle and attribute. Press Enter to accept the selection.
- Click the **Select in graphics area** icon under the **Base point** section.
- Select the lower quadrant point of the circle to define the base point of the block.

- Uncheck the **Edit in block editor** option. Next, select the **Remove from drawing** option from the **Entities** section and click **OK**.
- On the ribbon, click **Insert > Block > Insert**. Next, select the **Grid Bubble** block from the **Name** drop-down.
- Type **0** in the **Angle** box and click **OK**.
- Select the top endpoint of the first vertical grid line. The **Edit Attributes** dialog pops up.
- Type-in **A** in the GRIDBUBBLE box and press ENTER.

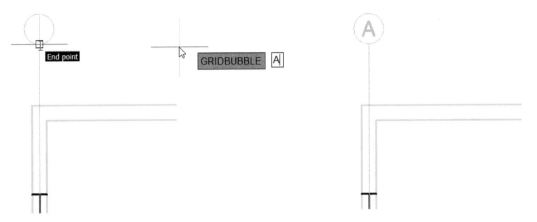

- Likewise, add other grid bubbles to the vertical grid lines.

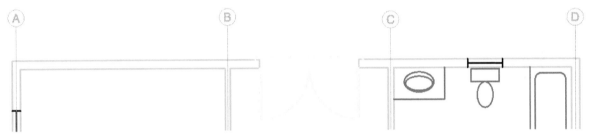

- Create another block with the name Vertical Grid bubble. Make sure that you select the right quadrant point of the circle as the base point.

VERTICALGRIDBUBBLE

- Insert the vertical grid bubbles, as shown below.

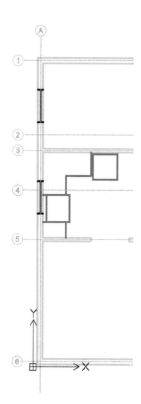

Adding Dimensions

- On the ribbon, click **Home > Layers > Layer Manager** drop-down > **Dimensions** to make it current.

- On the ribbon, click **Annotate > Dimensions > Dimension Style**.

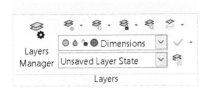 

- On the **Options – Drafting Styles** dialog, select **Standard** from the Style drop-down. Next, click the **New** button.

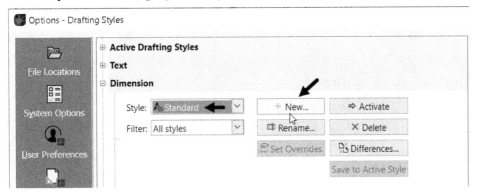

- Type-in Floor Plan in the **Name** box and click **OK**.

- Expand the **Linear Dimension** node and select **Format > Architectural**.

- Set **Precision** to **0'-01/16"**.

- Set **Fractional display** to **Horizontal**.

- Enter **0** in the **Round to the nearest** box.

 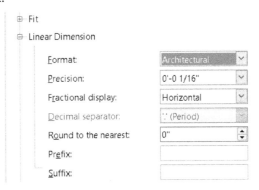

- Expand the **Arrows** node. Next, select **Start arrow > Architectural tick** and **End arrow > Architectural tick**.

- Select **Leader arrow > Closed Filled** and enter 1/4' in the **Size** box.

- Expand the **Line > Extension line settings** node and set **Offset** and **Distance past dimension line** to 3".

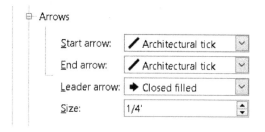

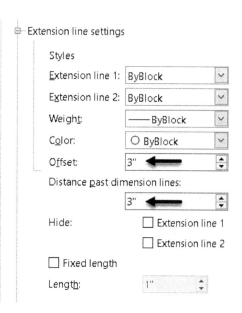

- Expand the **Text > Text Settings** node and set **Height** to 6″.

- Expand the **Text > Text position** node, set the following settings.

  Horizontal-Centered

  Vertical-Centered

- Expand the **Text > Text alignment** node, and then select the **Align with dimension lines** option.

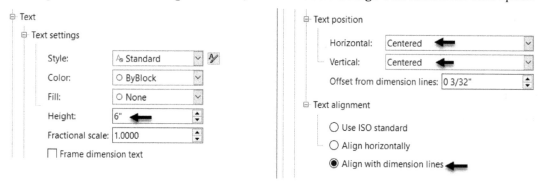

- Scroll upwards and click the **Activate** button. Next, click **OK**.

- On the ribbon, click **Annotate > Dimension > Dimension**.

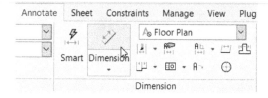

- Select the points on the vertical grid lines, as shown below. Next, move the pointer and click to locate the dimension.

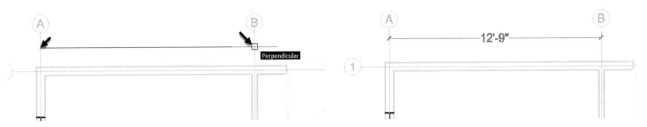

- On the ribbon, click **Annotate > Dimensions > Continue**. You will notice that a dimension is attached to the pointer

- Move the pointer and click on the next grid line.

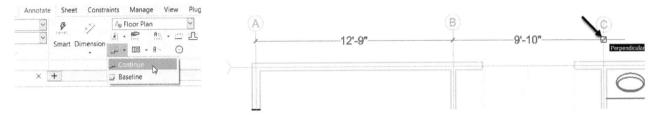

- Likewise, move the pointer and click on the next grid line.

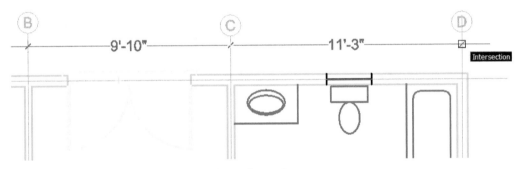

- On the ribbon, click **Annotate > Dimension > Smart**.

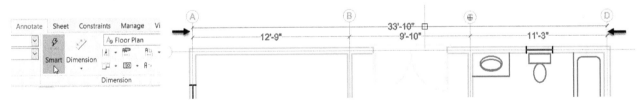

- Likewise, add vertical dimensions to the grid lines.

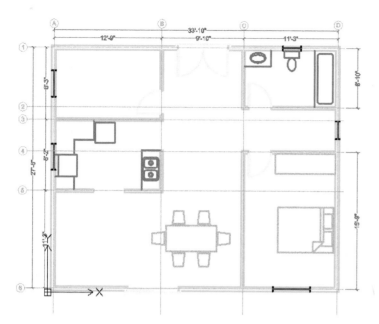

- Complete adding dimensions to the drawing, as shown below.

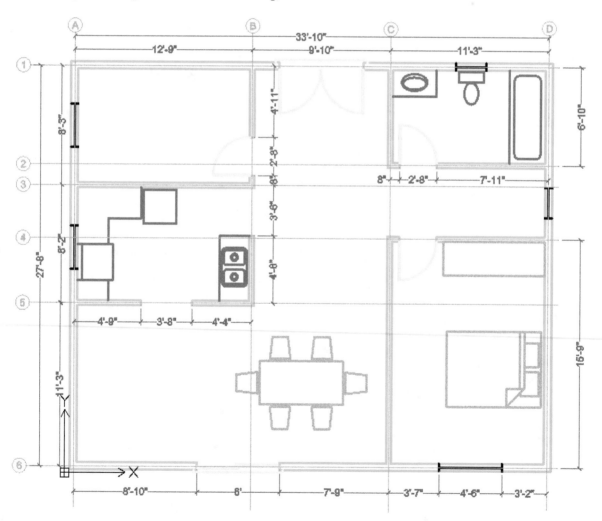

- Save and close the drawing.

Tutorial 2: Creating the Stairs

In this tutorial, you will draw stairs.

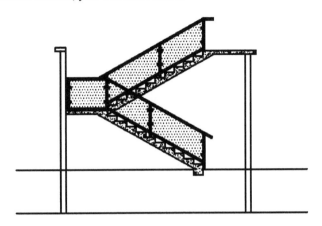

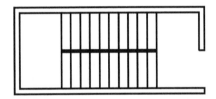

Staircase Nomenclature

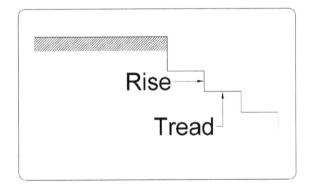

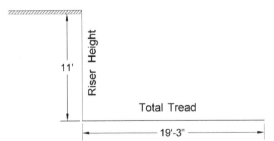

Creating the Stairs

- Start a new CorelCAD file using the **standard** template. Next, set the **Workspace** to **Drafting & Annotation**.

- Type **UN** in the command window and press Enter.

- On the **Drawing Settings** dialog, select **Type > Architectural** from the **Length** section.

- Select **Precision > 0-01/16**. Next, set the **Block units format** to **Inches**, and click **OK**.

- Type LIMITS in the command window and press Enter.

- Press Enter to accept 0, 0 as the lower limit.

- Type 50', 40' in the command window, and press Enter. The program sets the upper limit of the drawing.

- On the ribbon, click the **View** tab > **Navigate** panel > **Zoom** drop-down > **Zoom Bounds**.

- Deactivate the **Grid** icon on the status bar.

- Click the **Ortho** icon on the Status bar.
- Click the **Polyline** tool on the **Draw** panel of the **Home** ribbon tab.
- Click to define the start point of the line. Next, move the pointer toward the left.
- Type 17'8" and press ENTER.

- Move the pointer upward. Next, type 7' and press ENTER.
- Move the pointer toward the right. Next, type 17'2" and press ENTER.

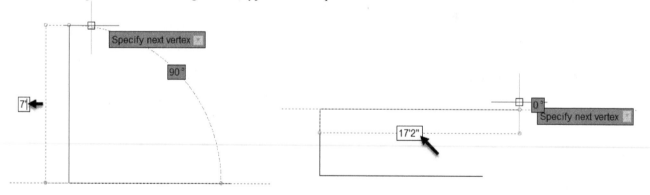

- Move the pointer downward. Next, type 3'6" and press ENTER.
- Press Esc.

- Click the **Offset** icon on the **Modify** panel of the **Home** ribbon tab. Next, type 6" and press ENTER.
- Select the polyline. Next, move the pointer outward and click.
- Click the **Line** tool and close the open ends of the drawing, as shown.

- Create a selection window across all the elements of the drawing.

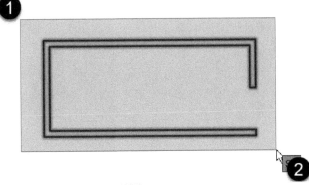

- Click the **Explode** icon on the **Modify** panel of the **Home** ribbon tab. The polylines are exploded into lines.
- Click the **Offset** icon on the **Modify** panel of the **Home** ribbon tab. Next, type 4' and press ENTER.
- Select the left vertical inner edge. Next, move the pointer toward the right and click.

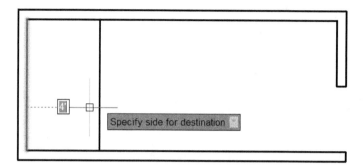

- Press ENTER.

- On the **Home** tab of the ribbon, click **Modify** panel > **Pattern** ⊞ . Next, click the **Path** tab on the **Pattern** dialog.
- Click the **Specify entities** icon and select the offset line and press ENTER.
- Click the **Specify path** icon and select on the inner horizontal line at the location, as shown.

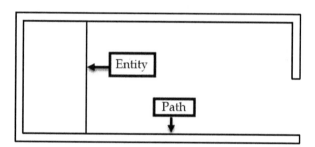

- Type **11** in the **Distance** and **Total number** boxes, respectively.

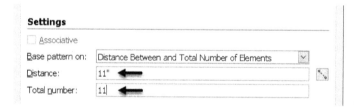

- Uncheck the **Use last entity selected** option and click the **Specify base point** icon.
- Select the left endpoint of the horizontal line, as shown.

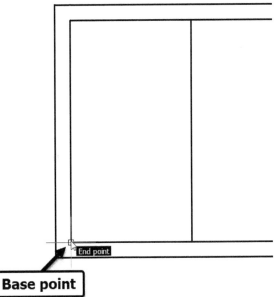

Base point

- Click the **OK** button to create the path pattern.
- Offset the inner horizontal lines by 3'5" distance in the inward direction.

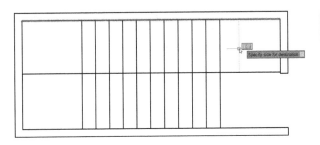

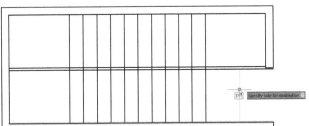

- On the **Home** tab of the ribbon, click **Modify** panel > **Trim/Extend** drop-down > **Trim**. Next, press ENTER.
- Select the portions of the horizontal lines, as shown.

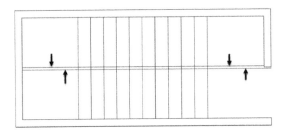

- Zoom-in to the center portion of the stairs. Click on the portions of the vertical lines, as shown.

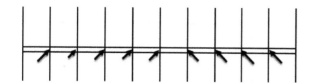

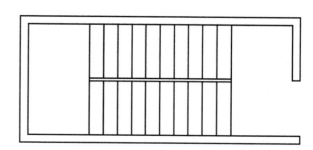

Creating the Section elevation of the Staircase

- Create a horizontal line above the staircase, as shown.
- Click the **Offset** icon on the **Modify** panel of the **Home** ribbon tab. Next, type **4'** and press ENTER.
- Select the newly created horizontal line. Move the pointer upward and click.

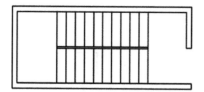

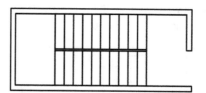

- On the ribbon, click **Line** drop-down > **Inifinite line**. Next, right-click and select the **Vertical** option.
- Select the corners of the drawing, as shown. Next, press ESC.

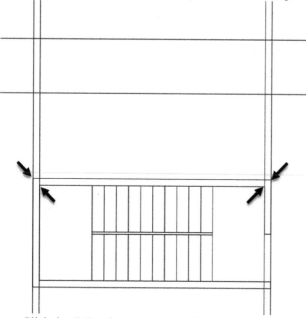

- Click the **Offset** icon on the **Modify** panel of the **Home** ribbon tab. Next, type **11'** and press ENTER.
- Select the offset horizontal line. Next, move the pointer upward and click.

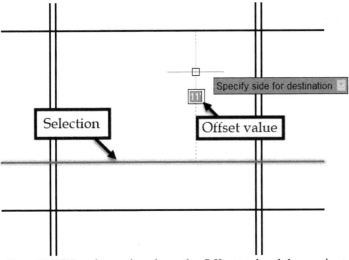

- Press ENTER twice to deactivate the **Offset** tool and then activate it again. Next, type 4" and press ENTER.
- Select the newly created offset line. Next, move the pointer upward and click.

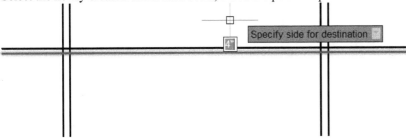

- On the **Home** tab of the ribbon, click **Modify** panel > **Trim/Extend** drop-down > **Power Trim**.
- Press and hold the left mouse button and drag the pointer across the portions of the construction lines, as shown.

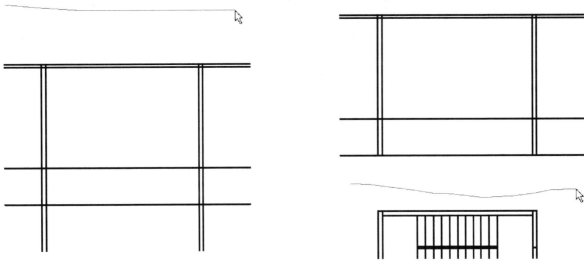

- Click the **Offset** icon on the **Modify** panel of the **Home** ribbon tab. Next, type 6" and press ENTER.
- Offset the outer vertical lines on both sides.

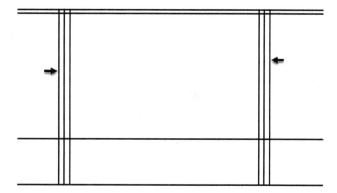

- On the **Home** tab of the ribbon, click **Modify** panel > **Trim/Extend** drop-down > **Trim**. Next, press ENTER.
- Trim the portions of the vertical and horizontal lines, as shown.

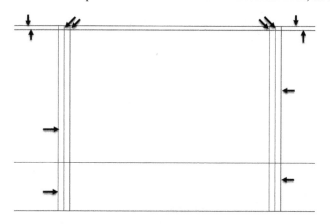

- On the **Home** tab of the ribbon, click **Modify** panel > **Trim/Extend** drop-down > **Extend**.
- Select the lower horizontal edge of the roof, as shown. Next, press ENTER.

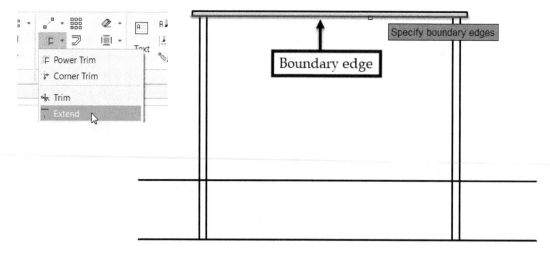

- Press and hold the left mouse button.
- Create a selection window across the lines of the staircase; the lines are extended up to the boundary edge.

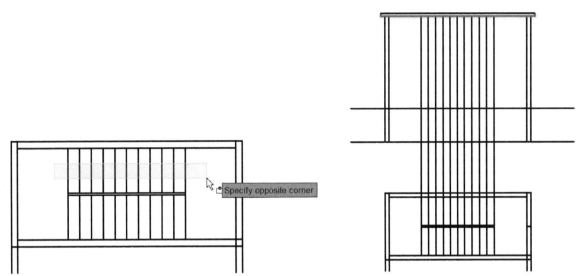

- On the **Home** tab of the ribbon, click **Modify** panel > **Trim/Extend** drop-down > **Trim**.
- Select the horizontal lines, as shown. Next, press ENTER.
- Create a selection window across the vertical lines, as shown.

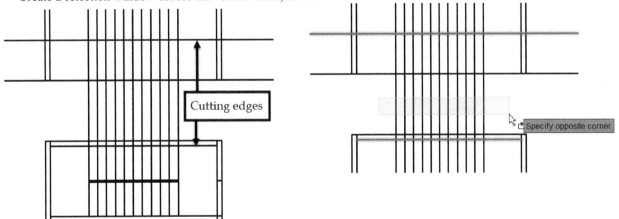

- On the **Home** tab of the ribbon, click **Draw** panel > **Polyline** . Next, select the first point of the polyline.
- Move the pointer upward. Next, type 6" and press ENTER.
- Move the pointer toward left. Next, type 11" and press ENTER.
- Press Esc.

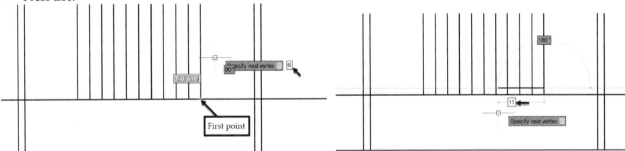

- Select the polyline and click the **Copy** icon on the **Modify** panel of the **Home** ribbon tab.
- Select the first point of the polyline as the base point.
- Move the pointer upward and select the endpoint of the polyline. The polyline is copied.

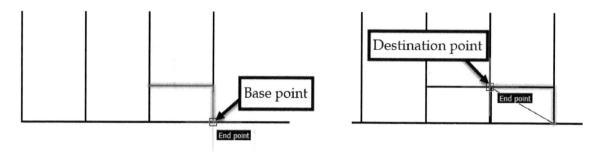

- Likewise, create copies of the polylines, as shown.

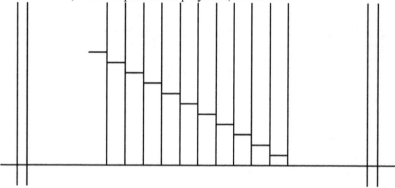

- Click the **Weld** icon on the **Modify** panel of the **Home** ribbon tab.
- Select all the polylines and press ENTER. All the polylines are joined.

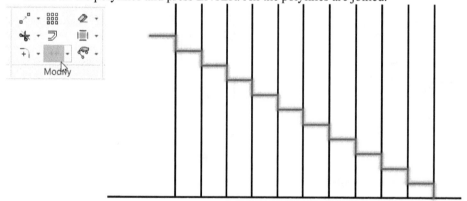

- On the **Home** tab of the ribbon, click **Modify** panel > **Trim/Extend** drop-down > **Extend**. Next, press ENTER.
- Click on the end portion of the polyline to extend it up to the left vertical line. Press Esc.

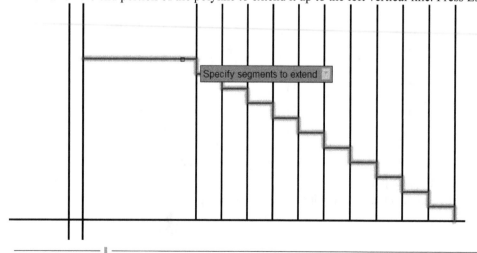

- Select the stairs and click **Copy** drop-down > **Mirror** on the **Modify** panel of the **Home** ribbon tab.
- Specify the start point of the mirror line, as shown.
- Move the pointer toward the left and specify the endpoint of the mirror line, as shown. Next, select **No**.

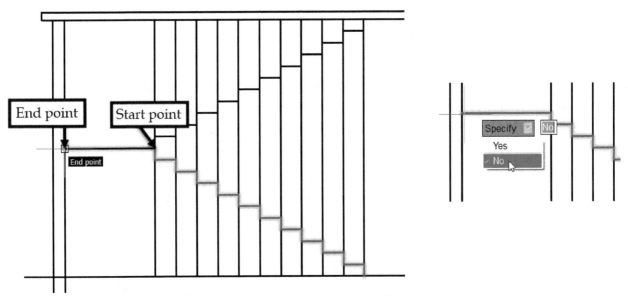

- Select the mirrored polyline. Next, click on the endpoint of the polyline.
- Move the pointer toward the right and select the vertex point, as shown. The polyline is shortened.

- Press Esc to deselect the mirrored polyline.
- Drag a selection window across the vertical lines from right to left, as shown.

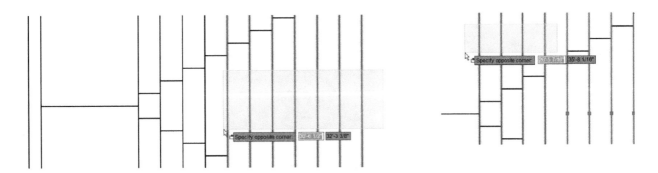

- Press Delete on your keyboard.
- On the **Home** tab of the ribbon, click **Draw** panel >**Line**. Next, select the corner points, as shown.
- Offset the newly created line by 4".

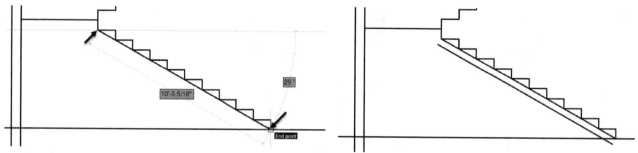

- On the **Home** tab of the ribbon, click **Draw** panel > **Line**. Next, press and hold the Shift key and right click.
- Select the **From** option from the **ESnap** menu. Next, select the point, as shown.
- Place the pointer on the vertical line. Next, press the TAB key and type 4".
- Press ENTER to specify the start point of the line.
- Move the pointer toward the left and click to create a horizontal line.

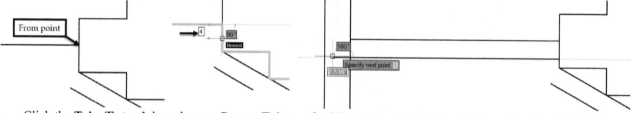

- Click the **Trim/Extend** drop-down > **Corner Trim** on the **Modify** panel. Select the horizontal and inclined lines, as shown.

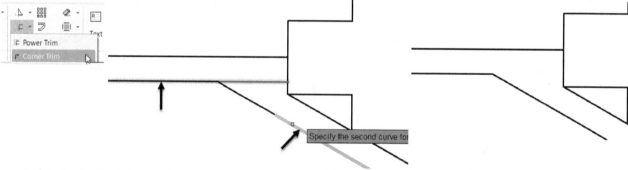

- Delete the inclined line, as shown.

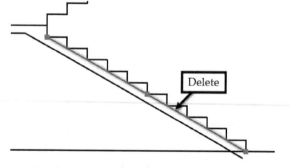

- On the **Home** tab of the ribbon, click **Draw** panel > **Line**. Next, select the corner point of the stair, as shown.
- Move the pointer downward. Next, type 1' and press ENTER.
- Move the pointer toward the right. Next, type 11" and press ENTER.
- Move the pointer upward. Next, type 6" and press ENTER.

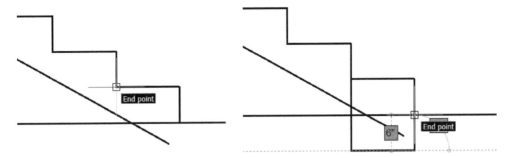

- On the **Home** tab of the ribbon, click **Modify** panel > **Trim/Extend** drop-down > **Trim**. Next, press ENTER.
- Select the portions of the lines, as shown.

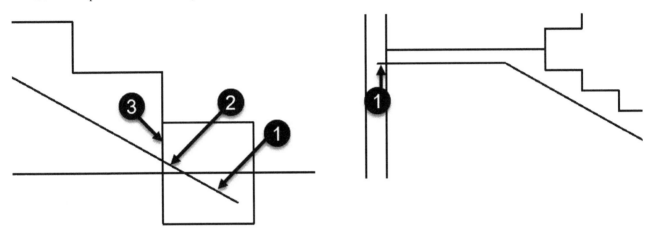

- On the **Home** tab of the ribbon, click **Draw** panel > **Line**. Select the corner points, as shown.
- Offset the newly created line by 4".

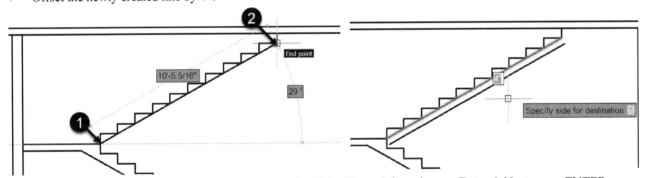

- On the **Home** tab of the ribbon, click **Modify** panel > **Trim/Extend** drop-down > **Extend**. Next, press ENTER.
- Select the inclined line, as shown.
- Extend the inclined line up to the horizontal line, as shown.

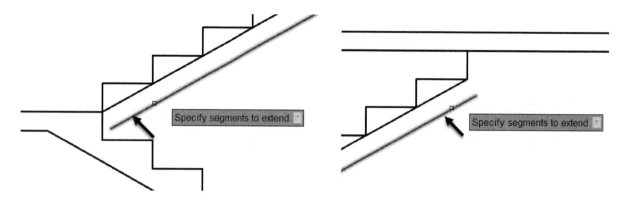

- Extend the vertical lines, as shown. Next, press Esc.

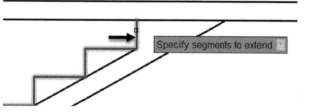

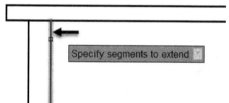

- Select the inclined line, as shown. Next, press Delete.

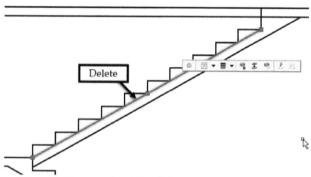

- On the **Home** tab of the ribbon, click **Modify** panel > **Trim/Extend** drop-down > **Power Trim**.
- Click and drag the pointer across the entities, as shown.

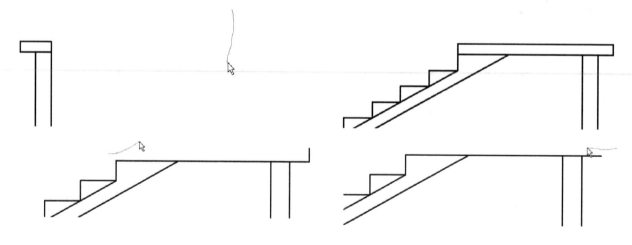

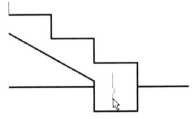

- Offset the horizontal line by 4" in the downward direction.
- Trim the elements, as shown. Next, activate the **Line** command and close the end of the offset line.

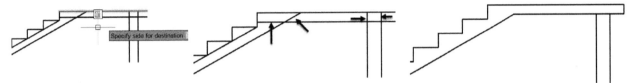

- On the **Home** tab of the ribbon, click **Draw** panel > **Hatch** drop-down > **Hatch**.
- On the **Hatch Creation** tab, select Predefined from the Hatch pattern type drop-down.
- Select the **AR-CONC** pattern from the **Pattern** drop-down from the **Pattern** panel.

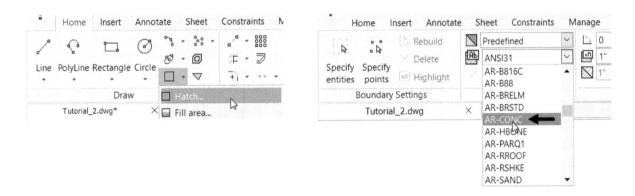

- Click the **Specify points** icon under the **Boundary Settings** panel. Next, pick points in the areas, as shown.

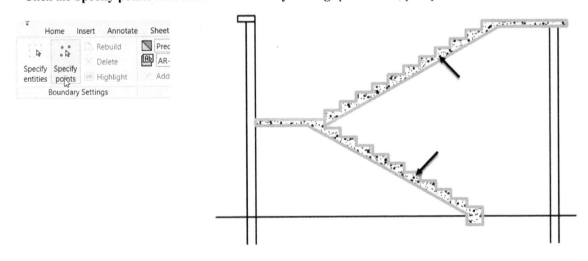

- Type 0.025 in the **Scale** box available in the **Properties** panel.
- Press ENTER to create the hatch pattern.

Creating the Handrail

- On the **Home** tab of the ribbon, click **Draw** panel > **Line**.
- Create two vertical lines of 3' length each at the locations, as shown.
- Activate the **Line** tool and connect the endpoints of the two vertical lines, as shown.

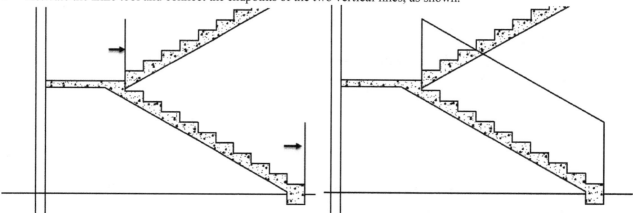

- On the ribbon, click **Home** tab > **Modify** panel > **Fillet** drop-down > **Change Length**.

- Right-click and select **Increment**. Next, type 12" and press ENTER.
- Click near the endpoint of the inclined line. The inclined line is lengthened.

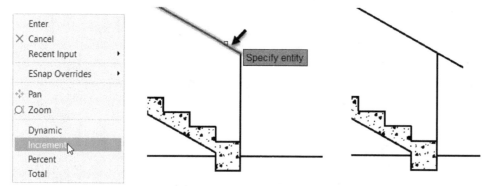

- Create a horizontal line, as shown.
- Click the **Offset** icon on the **Modify** panel. Next, offset the newly created lines by 2" distance, as shown.

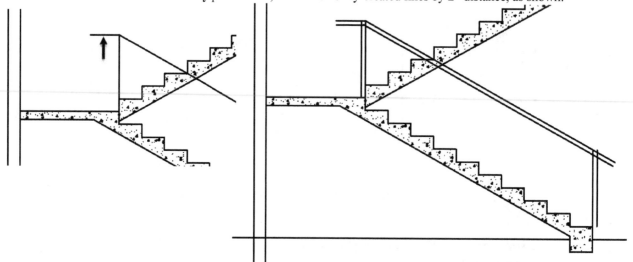

- On the **Home** tab of the ribbon, click **Modify** panel > **Trim/Extend** drop-down > **Extend**.
- Select the bottom horizontal edge as the boundary edge, and then press ENTER.

- Select the two vertical lines; they are extended up to the bottom horizontal edge, as shown.

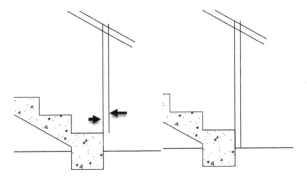

- Activate the **Line** tool. Next, zoom to the fifth step from the top.
- Press and hold the Shift key and right click. Next, select the **Mid between 2 Points** option.
- Select the two endpoints of the step; the start point of the line is specified at the midpoint.

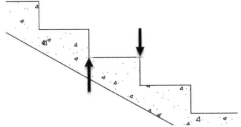

- Move the pointer upward and click.
- Click the **Offset** icon on the **Modify** panel. Offset the newly created line by 1" on both sides, as shown.
- Delete the middle line.

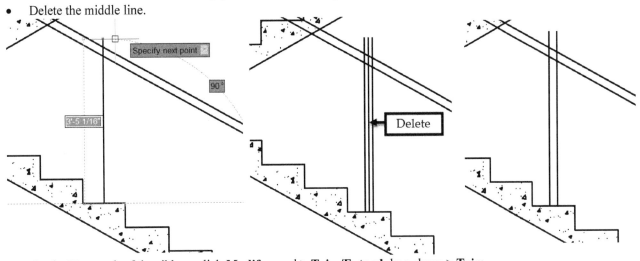

- On the **Home** tab of the ribbon, click **Modify** panel > **Trim/Extend** drop-down > **Trim**.
- Select the lower inclined and horizontal lines of the handrail. Next, press ENTER.
- Trim the portions of the vertical lines, as shown.

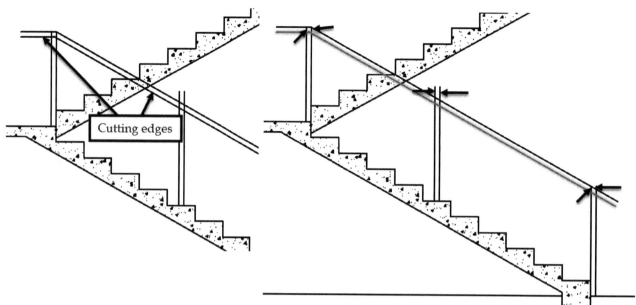

- On the **Home** tab of the ribbon, click **Modify** panel > **Trim/Extend** drop-down > **Corner Trim**.
- Select the unwanted portions of the lines, as shown.

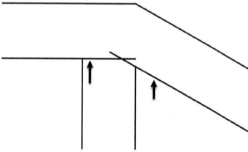

- On the ribbon, click **Home** tab > **Modify** panel > **Weld** drop-down > **Split at Point**.
- Select the vertical line, as shown.
- Press and hold the Shift key and right click. Select the **Midpoint** option.
- Select the midpoint of the vertical line, as shown. The vertical line is broken at the midpoint.

- On the **Home** tab of the ribbon, click **Draw** panel > **Rectangle** drop-down > **Corner**.
- Select the midpoint of the lower portion of the broken line, as shown.
- Right click and select the **Dimensions** option from the shortcut menu. Next, type -2 and press ENTER.
- Type 2 and press ENTER. Next, move the pointer upward and click.

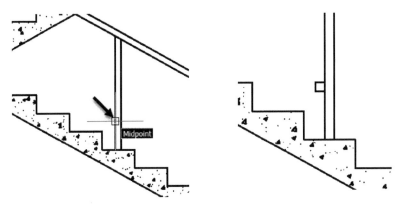

- Select the rectangle and click the **Copy** icon on the **Modify** panel.
- Select the top right corner point of the rectangle. Next, move the pointer upward.
- Select the midpoint of the upper portion of the broken line, as shown. Press ESC.

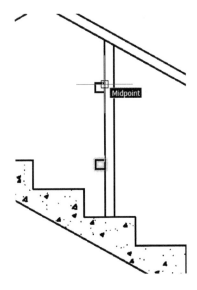

- Select the two rectangles and click the **Copy** icon on the **Modify** panel.
- Select the top right corner point of anyone of the rectangles.
- Move the pointer toward the right. Next, type 4" and press ENTER.

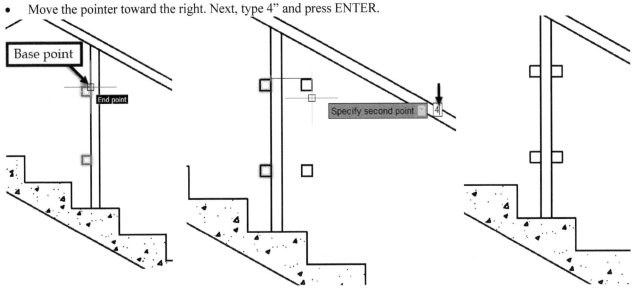

- Press Esc.
- Select the four rectangles and click the **Copy** icon on the **Modify** panel.
- Select the midpoint of the right vertical line.
- Move the pointer toward the right and select the midpoint of the vertical line, as shown.

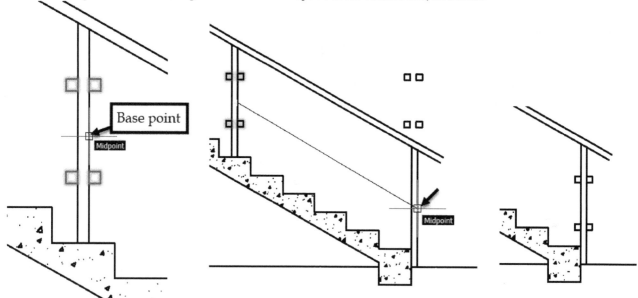

- Move the pointer toward the left and select the midpoint of the vertical line, as shown. Press Esc.

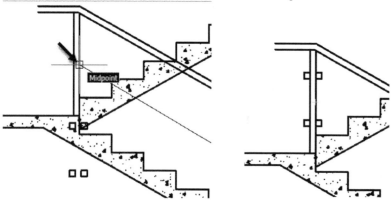

- Delete the two rectangles, as shown.

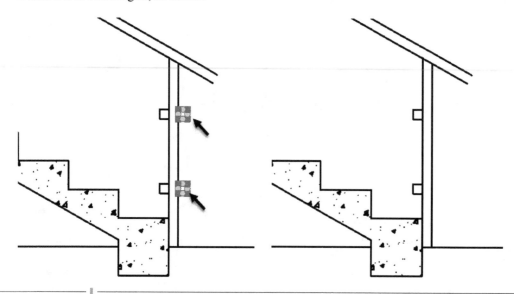

- Select the vertical line and click the **Offset** 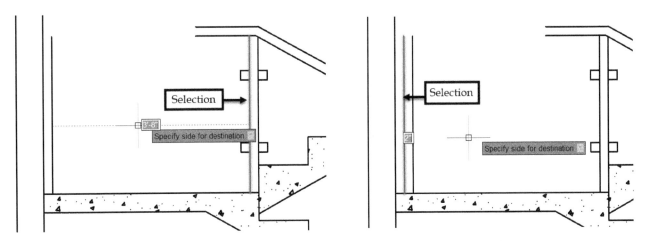 icon on the **Modify** panel.
- Type 3'8" and press ENTER. Next, move the pointer toward the left and click.
- Press ENTER twice.
- Type 2" and press ENTER. Next, select the newly offset line.
- Move the pointer toward the right and click.

- Click the **Trim/Extend** drop-down > **Corner Trim** icon on the **Modify** panel. Next, select the left vertical and top horizontal line, as shown.

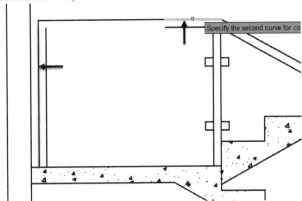

- On the **Home** tab of the ribbon, click **Modify** panel > **Trim/Extend** drop-down > **Extend** ⊤.
- Extend the horizontal line up to the vertical line. Press Esc.

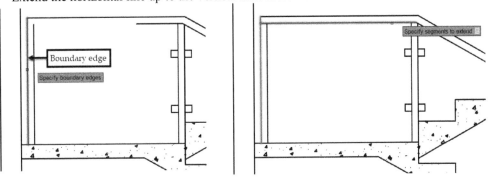

- Select the two rectangles and click the **Copy** ▫ icon on the **Modify** panel.
- Specify the base and destination points, as shown.

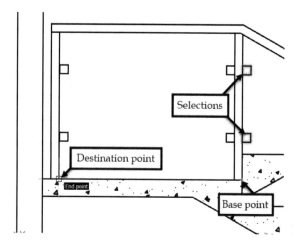

- Click the **Line** icon on the **Draw** panel. Next, select the corner points of the top and bottom steps, as shown.
- Press Esc.
- Select the newly created line and click the **Offset** icon on the **Modify** panel.
- Type 1" and press ENTER. Move the pointer upward and click.

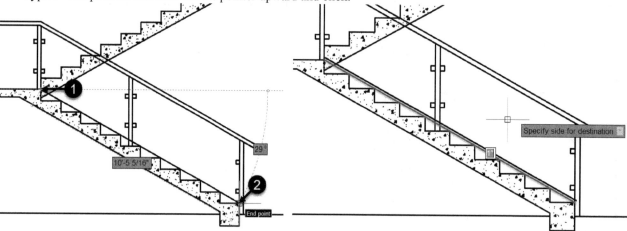

- Press ENTER twice. Next, type 2" and press ENTER.
- Select the newly offset line. Next, move the pointer upward and click.

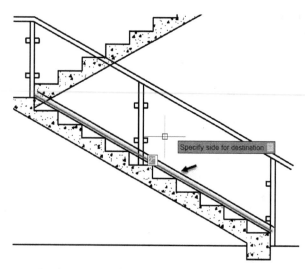

- On the **Home** tab of the ribbon, click **Modify** panel > **Trim/Extend** drop-down > **Trim**. Press ENTER.
- Trim the intersecting portions of the lines, as shown. Press Esc.

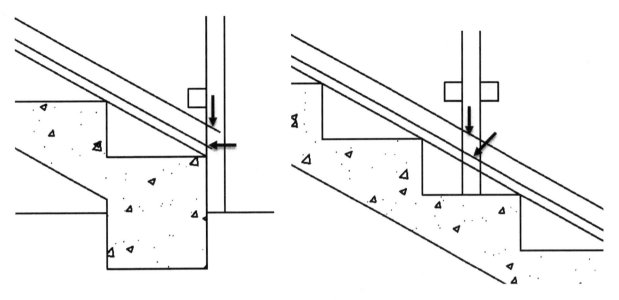

- Select the rectangles and click **Copy** drop-down > **Move** on the **Modify** panel. Next, specify the base point, as shown.
- Move the pointer upward. Next, type 4" and press ENTER.

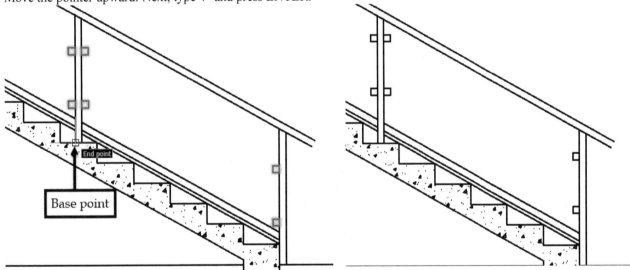

- Select the horizontal line, as shown. Next, click the **Offset** icon on the **Modify** panel.
- Type 33" and press ENTER. Next, move the pointer downward and click.
- Press ENTER twice. Next, type 2" and press ENTER.
- Select the newly offset line. Next, move the pointer upward and click.

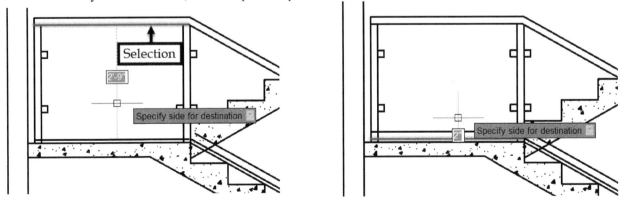

- Click **Trim/Extend** > **Corner Trim** on the **Modify** panel.
- Select the horizontal and inclined lines, as shown.
- Press ENTER and select the horizontal and inclined lines, as shown.

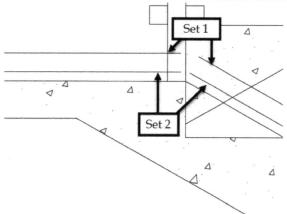

- Click **Trim/Extend** > **Trim** on the **Modify** panel. Next, press ENTER.
- Select the portions of the horizontal and inclined line, as shown.

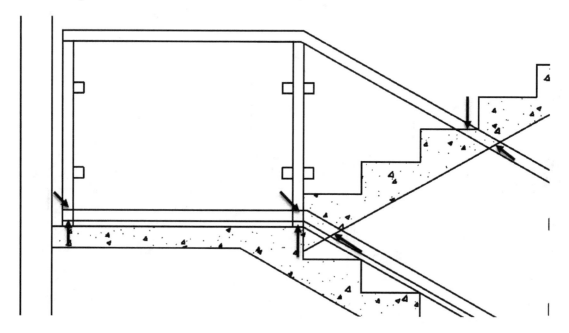

- Right-click and select the **eRase** option.
- Select the inclined lines, as shown. Next, press ENTER.

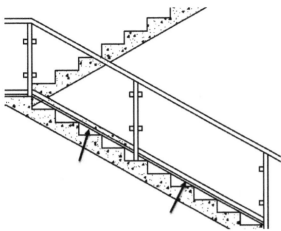

- Close the end of the offset lines using the **Line** tool.

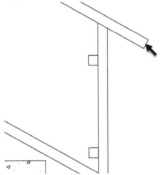

- Select the elements of the handrail.
- Click the **Copy** icon on the **Modify** panel. Next, Specify the base point, as shown.
- Move the pointer toward the right and click to create the copy.

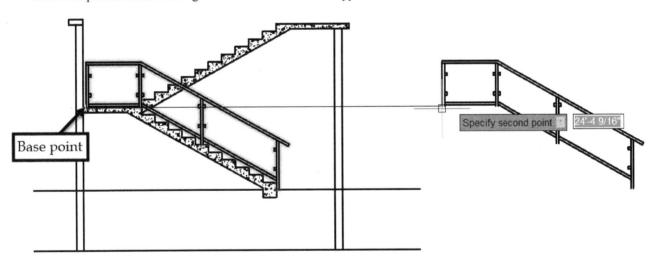

- Click the **Copy** drop-down > **Mirror** on the **Modify** panel.
- Create a selection window covering all the copied entities of the handrail. Next, press ENTER.
- Select the base point, as shown. Next, move the pointer vertically upward and click. Next, select **Yes**.

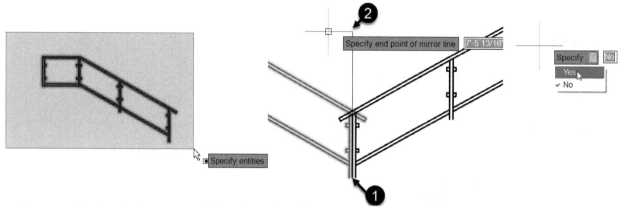

- Create a selection window across all the mirrored entities.
- Click the **Copy drop-down > Move** on the **Modify** panel. Next, specify the base point, as shown.
- Move the pointer toward the right and select the destination point.

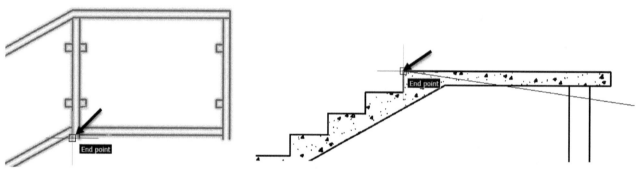

- Select the elements of the handrail, as shown. Next, press Delete.

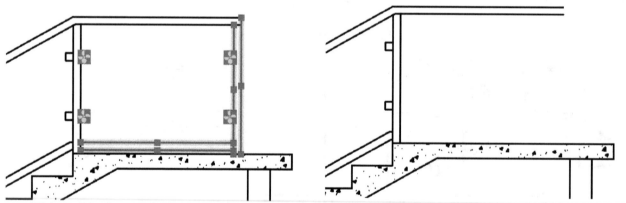

- Click the **Line** icon on the **Draw** panel. Next, press and hold the Shift key.
- Right click and select **From** from the **ESnap** menu. Next, select the corner point of the handrail, as shown.
- Move the pointer along the horizontal line, as shown.
- Press the TAB key and type 12. Next, press ENTER.
- Move the pointer downward and click.

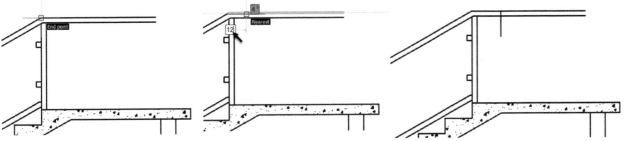

- Click the **Trim/Extend drop-down > Trim** icon on the **Modify** panel. Next, press ENTER.
- Trim the unwanted elements.

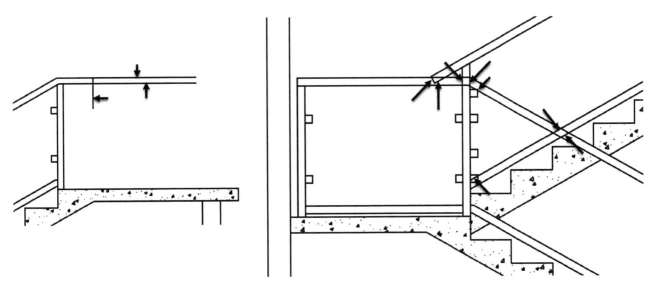

- On the **Home** tab of the ribbon, click **Draw** panel > **Hatch** drop-down > **Hatch**.
- On the **Hatch /Fill** dialog, click the **Preview patterns** ⬚ icon next to the **Pattern** drop-down,
- Select the **Sample** option from the **Select Pattern Style** dialog, and then select the **DOTS** pattern. Next, click **OK**.
- Type 50 in the **Scale** box under the **Angle and Scale** section.
- Click the **Specify points** icon under the **Boundary settings** section. Next, pick points in the areas, as shown.

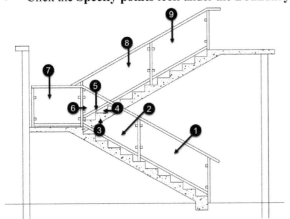

- Press ENTER and click **OK**.

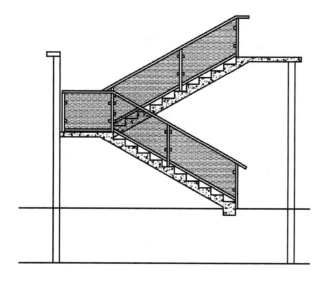

- Delete the construction lines, as shown.

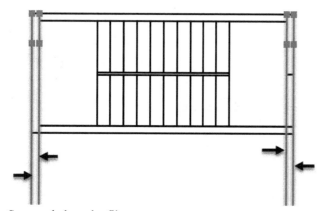

- Save and close the file.

Tutorial 3: Creating the Elevation View

In this tutorial, you will create the elevation view using the floor plan.

- Download the Elevation_plan from the companion website and open it.
- Click the **Layers Manager** icon on the **Layers** panel of the **Home** ribbon tab.
- Click the **New** icon on the **Layers Manager** palette. Next, type Elevation as the layer name.
- Double-click on the Elevation layer. Next, close the **Layers Manager** palette.
- Draw a horizontal line above the floor plan, as shown.

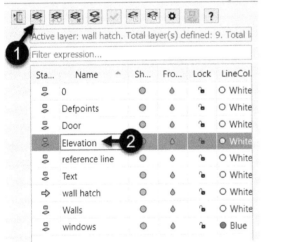

- On the ribbon, click **Home** tab > **Draw** panel > **Line** drop-down > **Ray**.
- Select the top-left corner of the floor plan. Next, move the pointer upward and click.

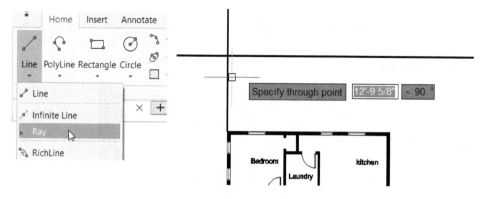

- Press ENTER twice.
- Select the top-right corner of the floor plan. Next, move the pointer upward and click.

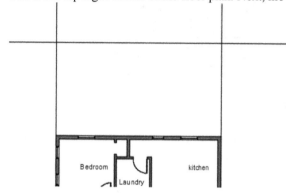

- Click the **Offset** 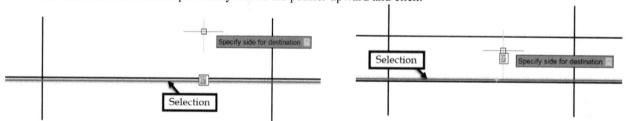 tool on the **Modify** panel of the **Home** ribbon tab.
- Type 6" and press ENTER. Next, select the horizontal line.
- Move the pointer upward and click to create an offset line. Next, press ENTER twice.
- Type 9' as the offset distance. Next, press ENTER.
- Select the offset line created previously. Move the pointer upward and click.

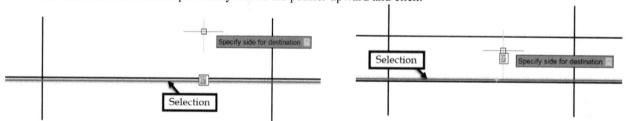

- Press ENTER twice.
- Type 10' as the offset distance. Next, press ENTER.
- Select the offset line created previously. Next, move the pointer upward and click.
- Press ENTER twice.
- Type 6' as the offset distance. Next, press ENTER.
- Select the offset line created previously. Move the pointer upward and click.

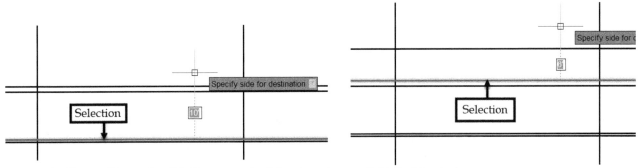

- On the **Home** ribbon tab, click **Draw** panel > **Line** drop-down > **Infinite Line** tool.
- Right click and select the **Offset** option from the shortcut menu.
- Type 16" as the offset distance. Next, press ENTER.
- Select the right exterior wall. Next, move the pointer toward the right and click.
- Select the left exterior wall. Move the pointer toward the left and click.

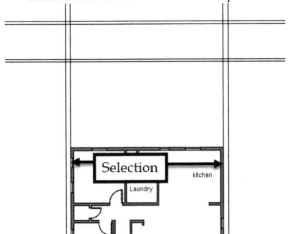

- Press ENTER twice.
- Right click and select the **Vertical** option.
- Select the corner point of the exterior wall, as shown.
- Press ENTER twice.
- Right click and select the **Offset** option from the shortcut menu.
- Type 16" as the offset distance. Next, press ENTER.
- Select the construction line created in the last step. Next, move the pointer toward the left and click.

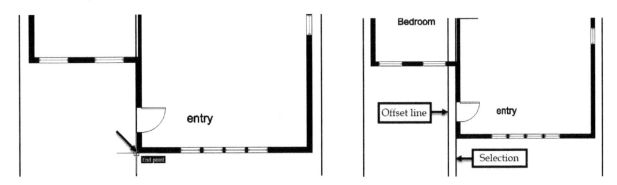

- On the **Home** ribbon tab, click **Modify** panel > **Weld** drop-down > **Split at Point**.
- Select the horizontal line, as shown.
- Select the intersection point between the horizontal and vertical lines, as shown.

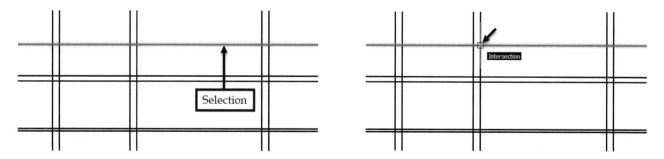

- Press ENTER to activate the **Split at Point** tool.
- Select the right portion of the broken line.
- Select the intersection point between the horizontal and vertical lines, as shown.

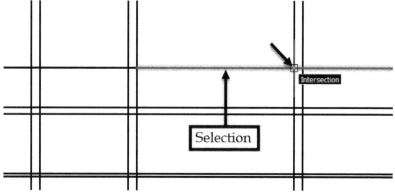

- Click the **Line** tool on the **Draw** panel of the **Home** ribbon tab.
- Select the midpoint of the broken line, as shown.
- Select the intersection point between the horizontal and vertical lines, as shown.

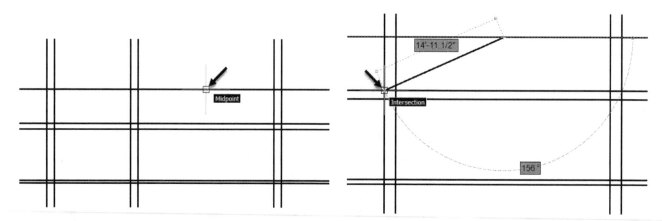

- Press ENTER twice. Next, select the start point of the line created in the last step.
- Select the intersection point between the horizontal and vertical lines, as shown.

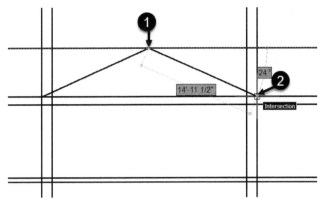

- Click **Trim/Extend** drop-down > **Trim** on the **Modify** panel of the **Home** ribbon tab. Next, press ENTER.
- Select the portions of the vertical lines, as shown.

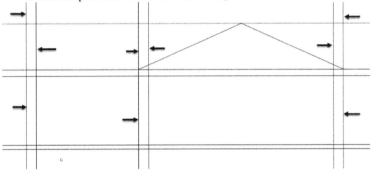

- Click **Home** > **Modify** > **Trim/Extend** drop-down > **Power Trim**.
- Click and drag the mouse pointer across the vertical lines, as shown.

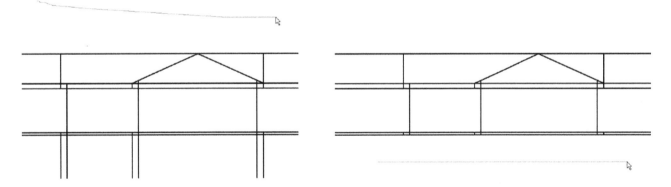

- Click **Home** > **Modify** > **Trim/Extend** drop-down > **Power Trim**.
- Trim the horizontal and vertical lines, as shown.

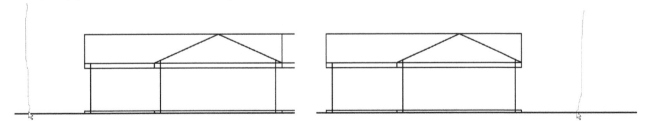

- Click **Home** > **Modify** > **Trim/Extend** drop-down > **Trim**. Next, press ENTER.
- Trim the small portions, as shown.

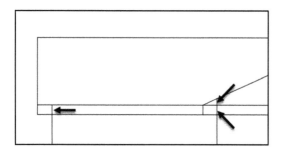
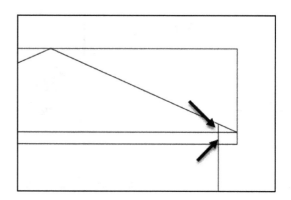

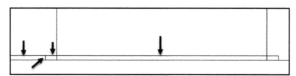

- Press Esc. Next, select the inclined line, as shown.
- Click the **Copy** ⊡ tool on the **Modify** panel of the **Home** ribbon tab. Next, specify the base point, as shown.
- Move the pointer downward and select the intersection point, as shown.

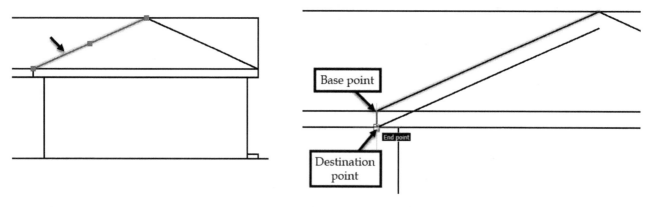

- Press Esc.
- Likewise, copy the other inclined line, as shown.

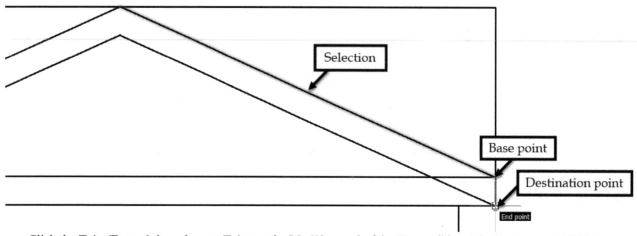

- Click the **Trim/Extend** drop-down > **Trim** on the **Modify** panel of the **Home** ribbon tab. Next, press ENTER.

- Select the portions of the horizontal line, as shown.

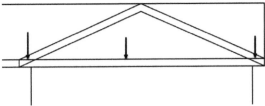

- On the **Home** ribbon tab, click **Modify** panel > **Weld** drop-down > **Split at Point**.
- Select the horizontal line, as shown. Next, select the intersection point, as shown.
- On the **Home** ribbon tab, click **Modify** panel > **Weld** drop-down > **Split at Point**.
- Select the vertical line, as shown. Next, select the intersection point, as shown.

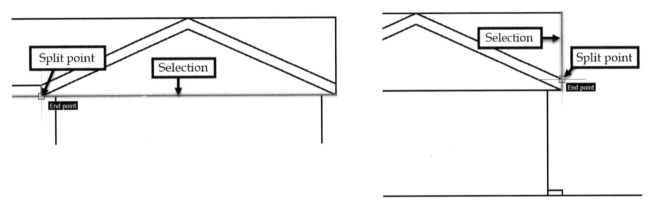

- On the **Home** ribbon tab, click **Modify** panel > **Weld** drop-down > **Split at Point**.
- Select the vertical line, as shown. Next, select the intersection point, as shown.
- Select the horizontal line, as shown. Next, press Delete.

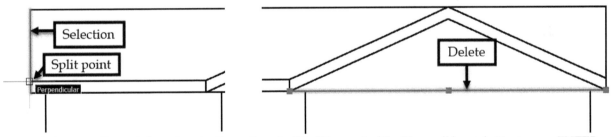

- Click the **Trim/Extend** drop-down > **Extend** on the **Modify** panel of the **Home** ribbon tab. Next, press ENTER.
- Select the two vertical lines, as shown.

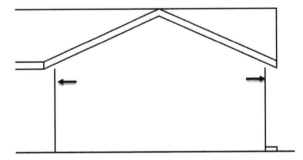

- Create a horizontal line connecting the endpoints of the two vertical lines.
- Select the two construction lines, as shown.
- Press Delete.

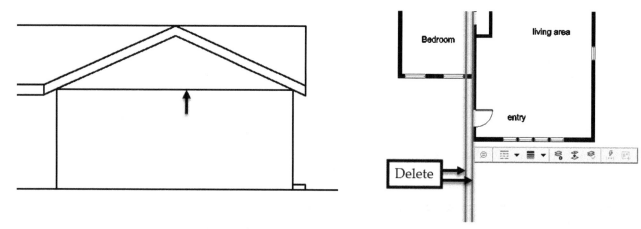

- On the **Home** ribbon tab, click **Draw** panel > **Line** drop-down > **Infinite Line** tool.
- Right-click and select the **Vertical** option.
- Zoom to the lower portion of the floor plan and select the vertex points on the window, as shown.

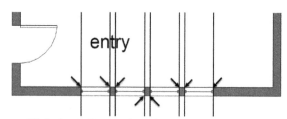

- Click the **Offset** tool on the **Modify** panel of the **Home** ribbon tab.
- Type 3' as the offset distance. Next, press ENTER.
- Select the horizontal line, as shown. Next, move the pointer upward and click.
- Click the **Rectangle** drop-down > **Corner** on the **Draw** panel of the **Home** ribbon tab.
- Select the intersection point, as shown.

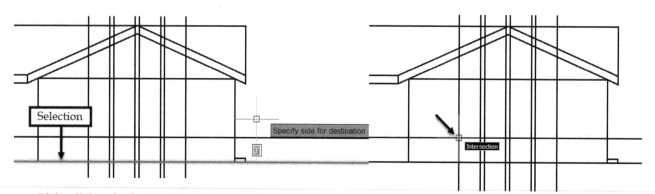

- Right-click and select the **Dimensions** option.
- Select the two intersection points, as shown.
- Type 54 as the rectangle width and press ENTER. Next, move the pointer upward and click.

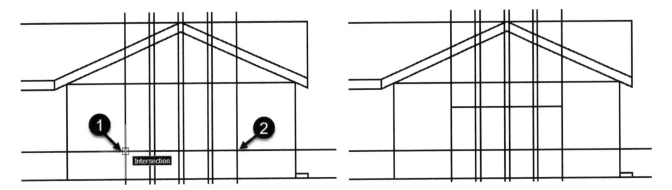

- Click the **Offset** tool on the **Modify** panel of the **Home** ribbon tab.
- Type 4" as the offset distance. Next, press ENTER.
- Select the rectangle. Next, move the pointer outward and click.

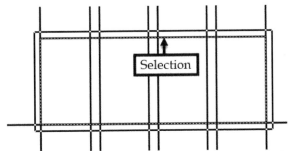

- Click the **Trim/Extend** drop-down > **Power Trim** on the **Modify** panel of the **Home** ribbon tab.
- Click and drag the pointer across the vertical lines, as shown.

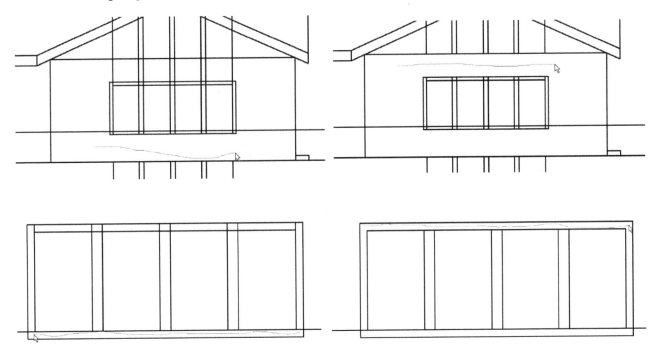

- Press ENTER.
- Select the vertical and horizontal construction lines, and then press Delete.

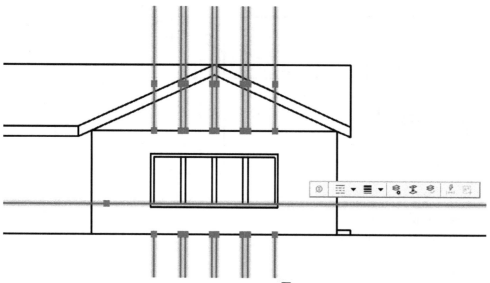

- Select the two rectangles and click the **Explode** tool on the **Modify** panel of the **Home** ribbon tab.

Explode

- On the ribbon, click **Home** tab > **Draw** panel > **Line** drop-down > **RichLine**.
- Right click and select the **Justification** option. Next, select the **Zero** option.
- Right click and the **Scale** option. Next, type 0.25, and press ENTER.

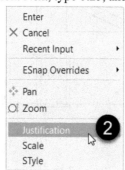
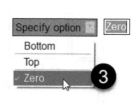
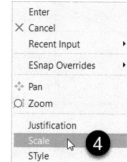

- Press and hold the Shift key, and then right click. Next, select the **Mid between 2 Points** option.
- Select the two points, as shown.
- Move the pointer downward and click.
- Press ENTER twice. Next, select the midpoint of the vertical line, as shown.
- Move the pointer toward the left and select the midpoint of the vertical line.

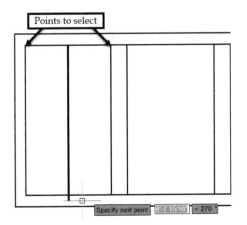
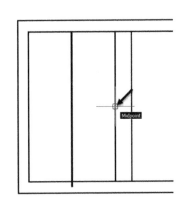
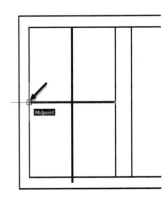

- Press Esc.
- On the ribbon, click **Home** tab > **Modify** panel >**Polyline Edit** drop-down > **RichLine**.
- Select the **Open Cross** option from the **Edit RichLines** dialog. Next, click **OK**.

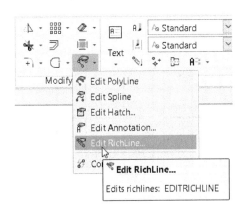

- Select the two richlines; the open cross is created at the intersection of the two richlines.

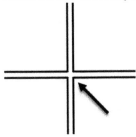

- Select the two richlines and click the **Explode** tool on the **Modify** panel of the **Home** ribbon tab.
- Click the **Trim/Extend** drop-down > **Power Trim** on the **Modify** panel of the **Home** ribbon tab.
- Click and drag the pointer across the unwanted portions of the richlines, as shown.

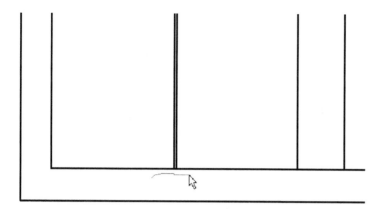

- Click the **Copy** tool on the **Modify** panel of the **Home** ribbon tab.
- Select the lines and press ENTER, as shown. Next, select the lower-left corner point.
- Move the pointer toward the right and select the corner point, as shown.
- Likewise, create two more copies of the multi-lines, as shown.

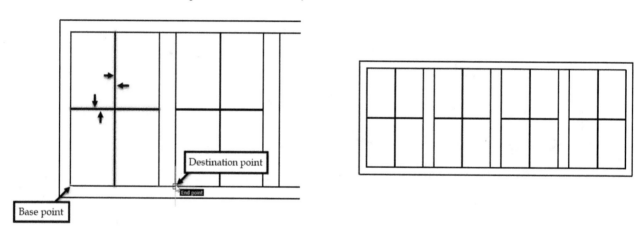

- Likewise, create two windows on the left side. Next, delete the construction lines.

- Click the **Hatch** tool on the **Draw** panel of the **Home** ribbon tab.
- On the **Hatch Creation** tab of the ribbon, select **Predefined** from the **Hatch Pattern type** drop-down on the **Pattern** panel.
- Select **AR-RSHKE** from the **Pattern** drop-down from the **Pattern** panel.
- Click the **Specify points** icon on the **Boundary Settings** panel and click in the regions, as shown.

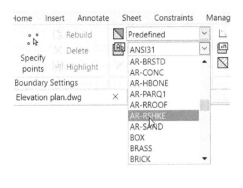
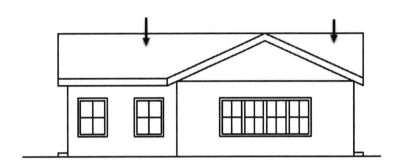

- Press ENTER.
- Click **Home > Draw > Hatch** on the ribbon. On the command bar, type T and press enter.
- On the **Hatch /Fill** dialog, click the **Preview patterns** ⬚ icon next to the **Pattern** drop-down,
- Select the **Sample** option from the **Select Pattern Style** dialog, and then select the **AR-B816** pattern. Next, click **OK**.
- Click the **Specify points** icon in the **Boundary Settings** section on the dialog, and then click in the regions, as shown.

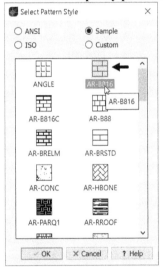
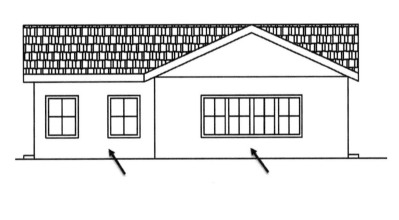

- Press ENTER.
- Click the **Additional Options** button on the bottom right corner of the **Hatch/Fill** dialog.
- Select the **Out** option from the **Internal regions** section. Next, click **OK** twice.

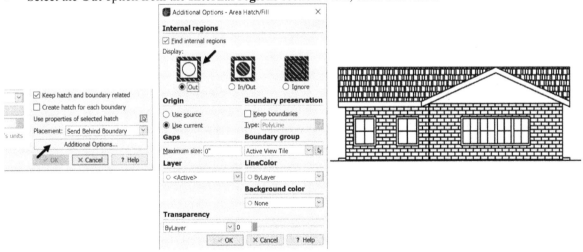

- Click the **Hatch** tool on the **Draw** panel of the **Home** ribbon tab.
- On the command bar, type T and press enter.
- On the **Hatch /Fill** dialog, select **ANSI31** from the **Pattern** drop-down,
- Enter **135** and **50** in the **Angle** and **Scale** boxes, respectively. Click in the region, as shown.

- Press ENTER twice.
- Save and close the file.

Tutorial 4: Creating the Roof Plan

In this tutorial, you will create the Roof plan using the floor plan.

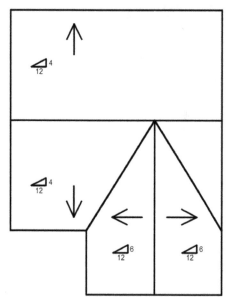

- Download the Floor_plan.dwg from the companion website.
- Start a new drawing using the **standard** template.
- Click the **Attach** tool on the **Reference** panel of the **Insert** ribbon tab.
- On the **Select file** dialog, go to the location of the Floor_plan.dwg file and double-click on it.
- Check the **Specify Later** option from the **Position** section.
- Click **OK** on the **Attach Reference Drawing** dialog. Next, click in the graphics window.
- Click **View** > **Navigate** > **Zoom** > **Zoom Fit** on the ribbon.

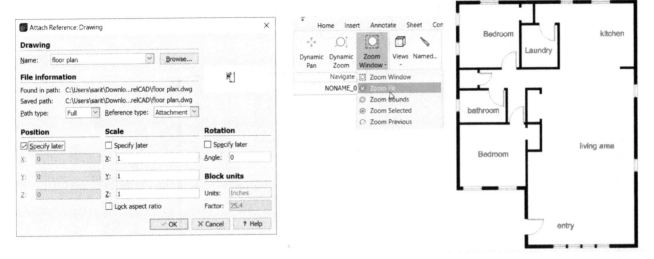

- Click the **Polyline** tool on the **Draw** panel of the **Home** ribbon tab.
- Select the corner points of the floor plan. Next, right-click and select the **Close** option.

- Click the **Offset** tool on the **Modify** panel of the **Home** ribbon tab. Next, type 16 and press ENTER.
- Select the newly created polyline. Next, move the pointer outward and click.
- Click the **Delete** tool on the **Modify** panel of the **Home** ribbon tab.
- Select the polyline used to create the offset. Next, press ENTER.

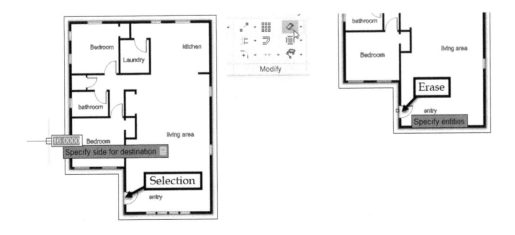

- Click the **Line** tool on the **Draw** panel of the **Home** ribbon tab. Next, select the midpoint of the left vertical line.
- Make sure the ORTHOMODE icon is active on the status bar.
- Move the pointer toward the right and click. Next, press ENTER twice.

- Select the midpoint of the lower horizontal line, as shown.
- Move the pointer upward and click.

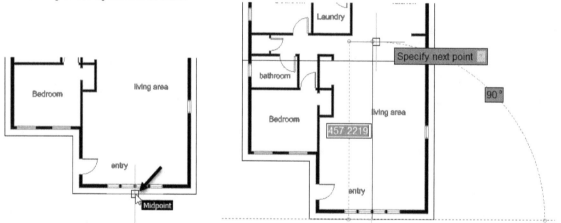

- Click the **Trim/Extend** drop-down > **Trim** tool on the **Modify** panel of the **Home** ribbon tab. Next, press ENTER.
- Select the unwanted portions of the lines, as shown.

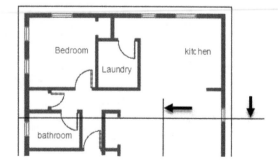

- Click the **Line** tool on the **Draw** panel of the **Home** ribbon tab. Next, turn OFF the **Ortho** button on the status bar.
- Select the corner point of the polyline.
- Select the intersection point of the vertical and horizontal lines. Next, press ESC.

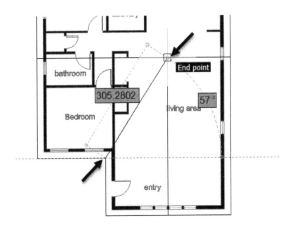

- Select the inclined line. Click the **Copy** drop-down > **Mirror** tool on the **Modify** panel of the **Home** ribbon tab.
- Select the endpoints of the vertical line. Next, select the **No** option.

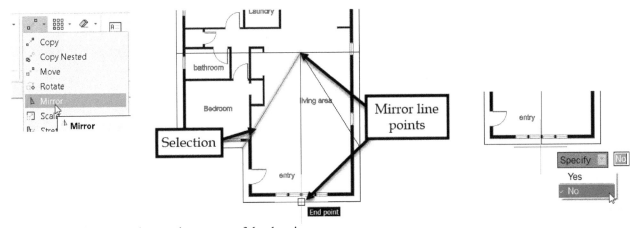

Next, you need to move the attachment out of the drawing.

- Select the attachment.
- Click on the origin point of the attachment, and then move the pointer upward, and click.

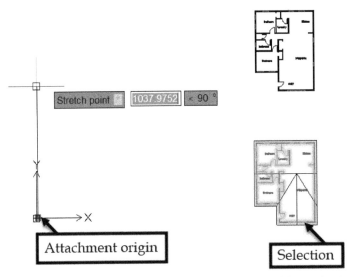

- Click the **Line** tool on the **Draw** panel of the **Home** ribbon tab. Next, click in the graphics window.
- Move the pointer toward the right. Next, type 36, and press ENTER.
- Move the pointer upward. Next, type 18, and press ENTER.

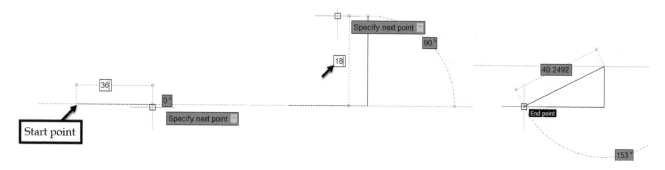

- Click the **Text** drop-down > **Simple Note** on the **Annotations** panel of the **Home** ribbon tab.
- Click in the graphics window.
- Type **12** as the text height. Next, press ENTER.
- Type 0 as the rotation angle, and then press ENTER.

- Type 4 and click in the graphics window.
- Type 12 and click in the graphics window. Next, press ESC.
- Select the 4 text and click on its base point. Next, move the pointer and click at the location, as shown.
- Likewise, position the 12 text at the location, as shown.

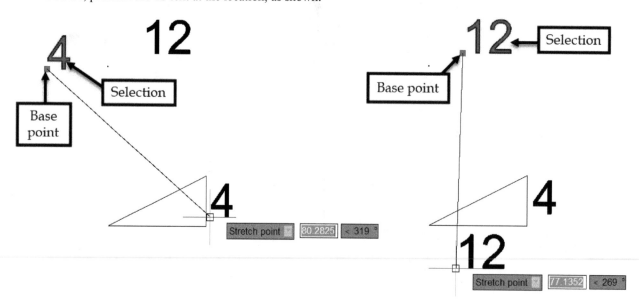

- Create a selection window across the triangle and the texts.
- Click the **Copy** tool on the **Modify** panel of the **Home** ribbon tab. Next, select the base point, as shown.

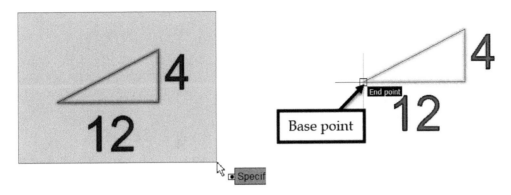

- Place the copies at the locations, as shown.

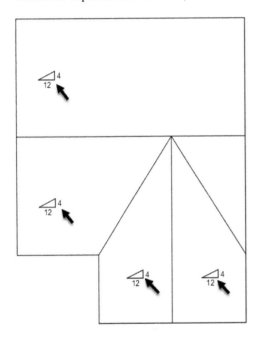

- Zoom the lower portion of the drawing. Next, double-click on 4.
- Type 6 and click in the graphics window.
- Likewise, change the text on the right side to 6. Next, press ESC.

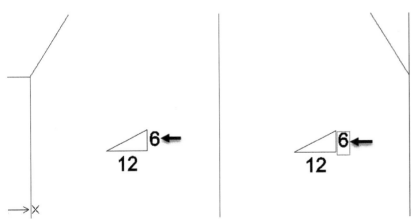

- Click the **Rectangle** drop-down > **Corner** on the **Draw** panel of the **Home** ribbon tab.
- Click at the location, as shown. Next, right-click and select the **Dimensions** option. Type 36 and press ENTER.
- Type -72 and press ENTER.

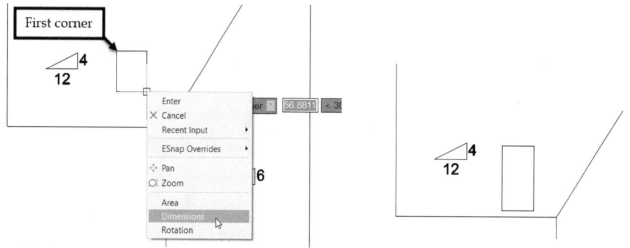

- Click the **Line** tool on the **Draw** panel of the **Home** ribbon tab. Select the midpoints of the horizontal edges of the rectangle.

- Press ENTER twice. Next, select the midpoint of the left vertical edge of the rectangle.
- Select the lower endpoint of the vertical line. Next, select the midpoint of the right vertical edge of the rectangle.
- Press ESC.
- Select the rectangle and press Delete.

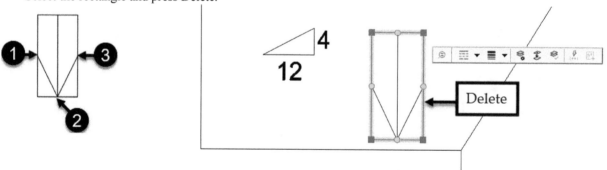

- Create a selection window across all the elements of the arrow.
- Click the **Copy** drop-down > **Mirror** on the **Modify** panel of the **Home** ribbon tab.
- Select the endpoints of the horizontal line to define the mirror line. Next, right-click and select **NO**.

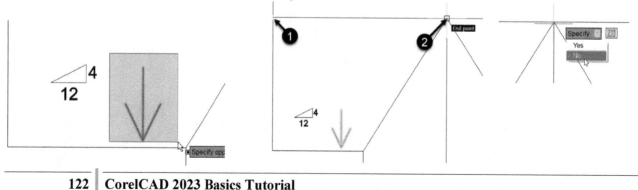

- Create a selection window across all the elements of the arrow.
- Click the **Rotate** tool on the **Modify** panel of the **Home** ribbon tab. Next, select the base point, as shown.
- Right-click and select the **Copy** option. Move the pointer vertically downward and click.

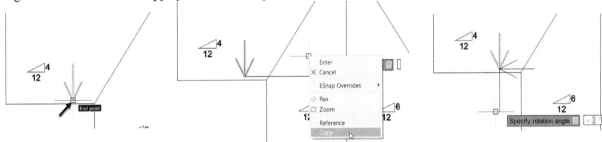

- Select the elements of the rotated arrow.
- Click **Copy** drop-down > **Move** tool on the **Modify** panel of the **Home** ribbon tab.
- Select the base point, as shown. Next, move the pointer toward the right and click.

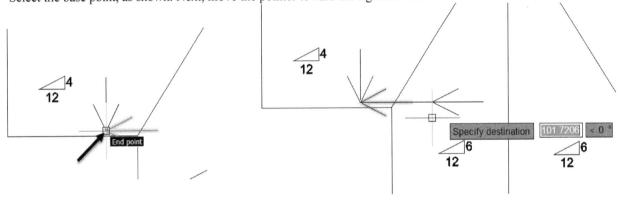

- Select the elements of the arrow moved in the previous step.
- Click the **Copy** drop-down > **Mirror** tool on the **Modify** panel of the **Home** ribbon tab.
- Select the endpoints of the vertical line, as shown.

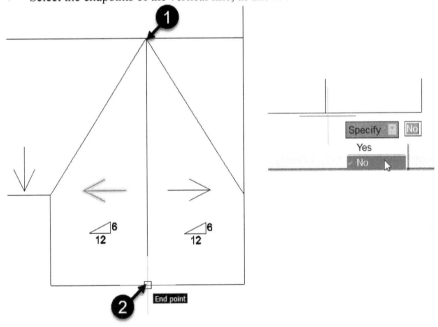

- Right-click and select **No**.
- Save and close the drawing file.

Tutorial 5: Creating the Wall and Roof Detail

In this tutorial, you will create the Roof and wall detail.

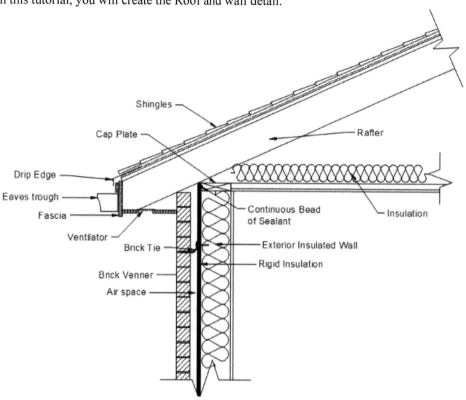

- Download the Roof_&_wall_detail.dwg file and open it.
- Click the **Layers Manager** tool on the **Layers** panel of the **Home** ribbon tab.
- Create a new layer and name it as Roof_wall_detail. Next, make the new layer are current.

- Close the **Layers Manager** palette on the right pane.
- On the **Home** ribbon tab, click > **Draw** panel > **Line** drop-down > **Ray** tool.
- Create the projection lines from the elevation view, as shown.
- Create a vertical line, as shown.

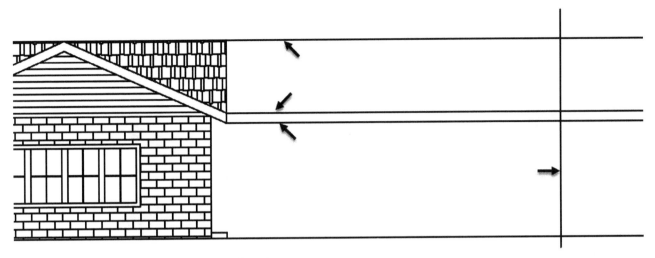

- Select the two inclined lines of the roof, as shown.
- Select the two vertical lines, as shown.

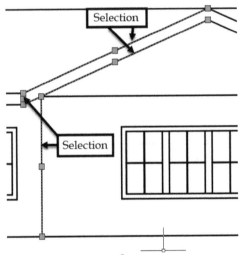

- Click the **Copy** ▫ tool on the **Modify** panel of the **Home** ribbon tab. Select the base point, as shown.
- Move the pointer toward the right and select the intersection point, as shown.

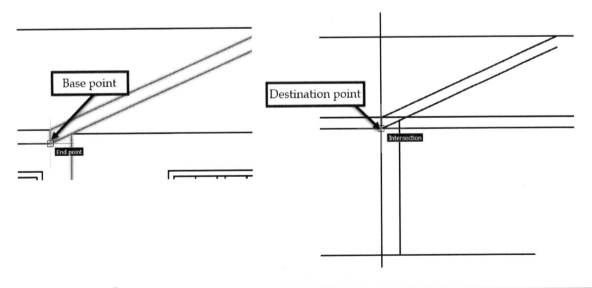

- Delete the reference lines, as shown.
- Click the **Trim** tool on the **Modify** panel of the **Home** ribbon tab. Next, press ENTER.
- Select the portion of the horizontal line, as shown.

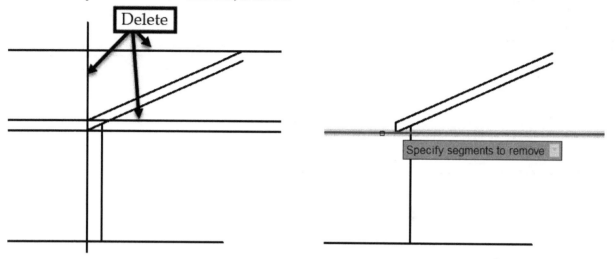

- Click the **Offset** tool on the **Modify** panel of the **Home** ribbon tab. Next, type 4, and press ENTER.
- Select the vertical line. Next, move the pointer toward the right and click.
- Press ENTER twice. Next, type 2, and press ENTER.
- Select the offset line. Next, move the pointer toward the right and click.

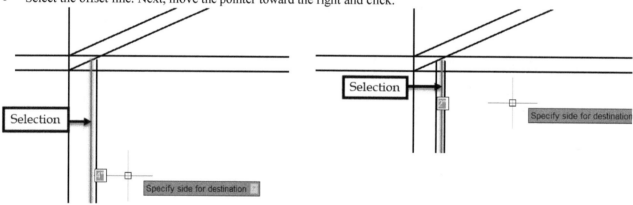

Creating the Brick Veneer

- Click the **Rectangle** drop-down > **Corner** on the **Draw** panel of the **Home** ribbon tab.
- Specify the corner point, as shown.
- Right-click and select the **Dimensions** option. Next, type 4, and press ENTER.
- Type -4 and press ENTER.

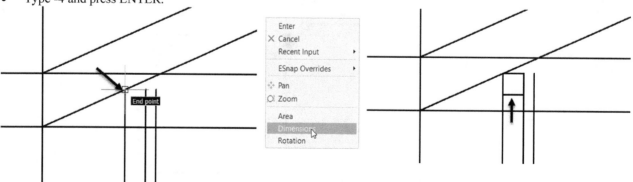

- Select the rectangle and click the **Pattern** icon on the **Modify** panel of the **Home** ribbon tab.

- Click the **Path** tab on the **Pattern** dialog.
- Click the **Specify path** icon on the **Pattern** dialog. Next, select the left vertical line to define the path.
- Select the **Distance Between and Total Number of Elements** option from the **Base pattern on** drop-down.
- Type **4.25** in the **Distance** box.
- Type **14** in the **Total number** box. Next, click **OK**.

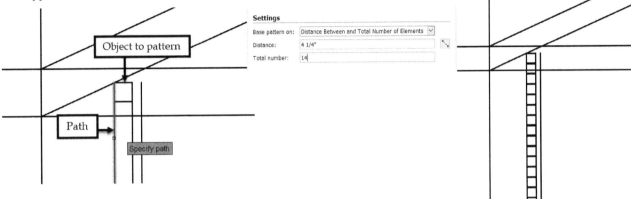

- Select any one of the rectangles.
- Right click and select **Select Matching** from the shortcut menu.

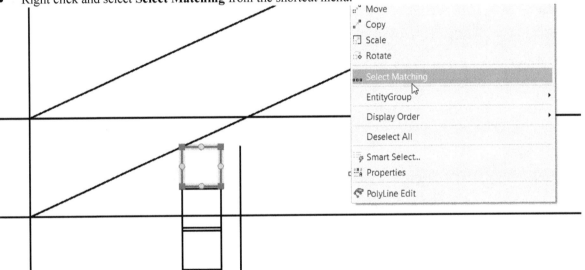

- Click the **Explode** tool on the **Modify** panel of the **Home** ribbon tab. All the rectangles are exploded into individual objects.
- Click the **Line** tool on the **Draw** panel of the **Home** ribbon tab. Next, zoom to the top portion of the drawing.
- Create a line by selecting the two points, as shown. Next, press ESC.
- Select the newly created line.
- Click the **Copy** drop-down > **Move** tool on the **Modify** panel of the **Home** ribbon tab.
- Select the top endpoint of the selected line. Next, move the pointer toward the right.
- Type 0.125, and press ENTER.

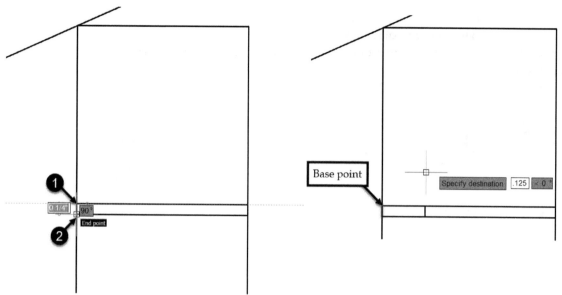

- Select the line moved in the last step.
- Click the **Pattern** icon on the **Modify** panel of the **Home** ribbon tab.
- Click the **Linear** tab on the **Pattern** dialog.
- In the **Settings** section, type **13** in the Number of elements on the **Vertical axis** box.
- Type **-4.25** in the Spacing between elements on the **Vertical axis** box.
- Type **2** in the Number of elements on the **Horizontal axis** box.
- Type **3.75** in the Spacing between elements on the **Horizontal axis** box.
- Click **OK**.

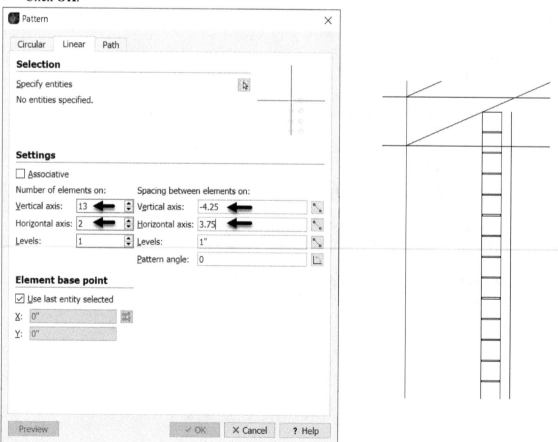

- Select the two vertical lines, as shown. Next, press Delete.

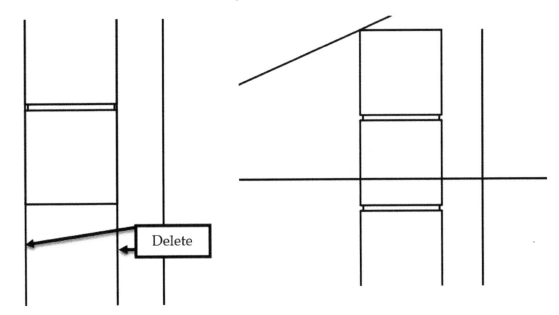

Delete

- Click the **Hatch** tool on the **Draw** panel of the **Home** ribbon tab.
- Select the **ANSI31** pattern from the **Pattern** drop-down.
- Type **8** in the **Scale** box in the **Angle and Scale** section.
- Click the **Specify points** icon in the **Boundary Settings** section and click in the regions, as shown.

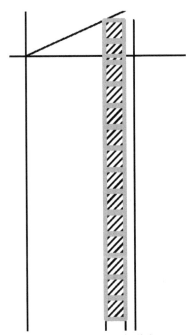

- Press and ENTER and click **OK**.

Creating the Brick Tie

- On the ribbon, click **View** tab > **Navigate** panel > **Zoom** drop-down > **Zoom Window**.
- Create a zoom window at the location, as shown.

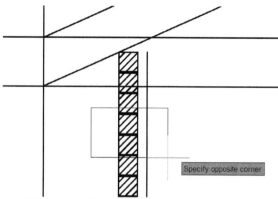

- Click the **Offset** tool on the **Modify** panel of the **Home** ribbon tab.
- Type 0.025, and press ENTER. Next, offset the two horizontal lines in the inward direction.

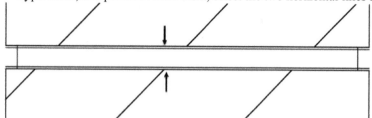

- Press ENTER twice.
- Type 1 and press ENTER. Next, offset the left vertical line towards the right.

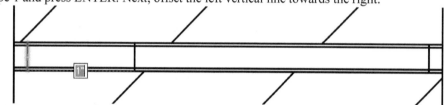

- Click the **Trim/Extend** drop-down > **Trim** tool on the **Modify** panel of the **Home** ribbon tab. Next, press ENTER.
- Trim the portions of the lines, as shown.

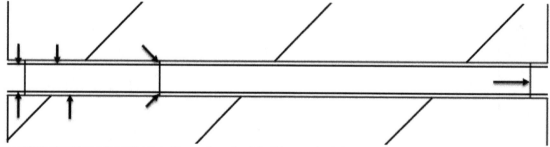

- Click the **Trim** drop-down > **Extend** on the **Modify** panel of the **Home** ribbon tab. Next, press ENTER.
- Select the ends of the horizontal lines, as shown. The horizontal lines are extended up to the right vertical line.

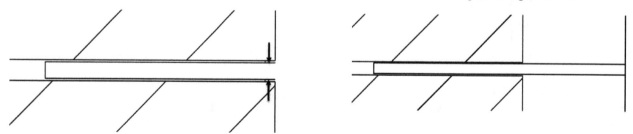

- Click the **Line** tool on the **Draw** panel of the **Home** ribbon tab.
- Select the endpoint of the lower horizontal line. Next, move the pointer vertically upward.

- Type 3 and press ENTER.
- Click the **Offset** tool on the **Modify** panel of the **Home** ribbon tab.
- Type 0.2 and press ENTER.
- Select the vertical line created in the last step.
- Move the pointer toward the left and click.

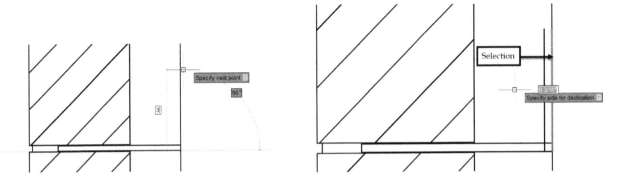

- Click the **Fillet** drop-down > **Chamfer** on the **Modify** panel of the **Home** ribbon tab.
- Right click and select the **Angle** option. Next, type 1 as the chamfer length.
- Type 45 as the chamfer angle. Next, select horizontal and vertical lines, as shown.
- Likewise, create another chamfer, as shown.
- Click the **Line** tool on the **Draw** panel of the **Home** ribbon tab. Next, cap the ends of the offset lines, as shown.

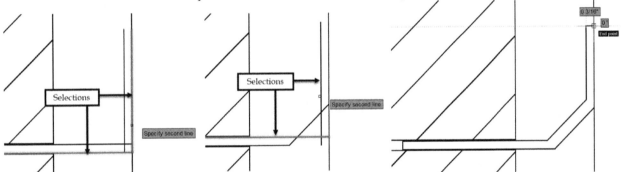

- Click the **Rectangle** drop-down > **Corner** on the **Draw** panel of the **Home** ribbon tab. Next, click in the graphic window.
- Right-click and select the **Dimensions** option. Next, type 0.2, and press ENTER.
- Type 0.5 and press ENTER.
- Select the rectangle and click the **Copy** drop-down > **Move** tool on the **Modify** panel of the **Home** ribbon tab.
- Select the midpoint of the right vertical edge of the rectangle.
- Move the pointer and select the midpoint of the vertical line, as shown.

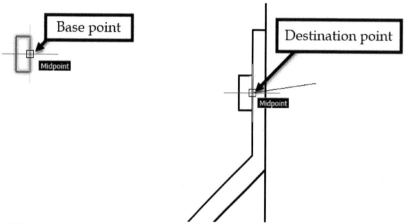

- Click the **Line** tool on the **Draw** panel of the **Home** ribbon tab.
- Select the midpoint of the right vertical edge of the rectangle. Next, move the pointer toward the right.
- Type 3.5 and press ENTER.
- Click the **Offset** tool on the **Modify** panel of the **Home** ribbon tab.
- Type 0.1 and press ENTER. Next, offset the newly created horizontal line on both sides.

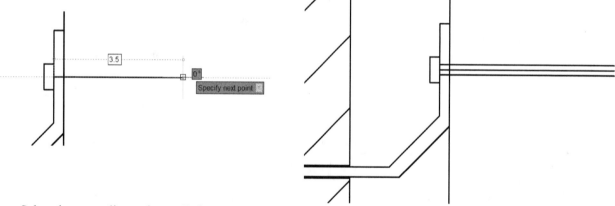

- Select the center line and press Delete.
- Click the **Arc** drop-down > **Start, End, Direction** on the **Draw** panel of the **Home** ribbon tab.
- Select the endpoints of the offset lines.
- Move the pointer toward the right and click.

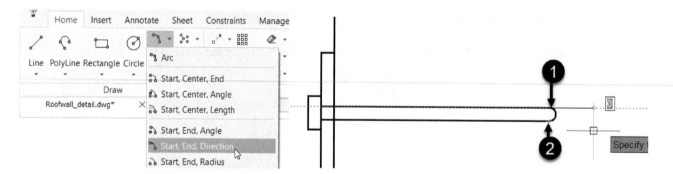

- On the ribbon, click **Home > Draw > Hatch** drop-down > **Hatch**. Next, enter T in the command bar and press Enter
- On the **Hatch /Fill** dialog, click the **Preview patterns** ⋯ icon next to the **Pattern** drop-down,
- Select the **Sample** option from the **Select Pattern Style** dialog, and then select the **SOLID** pattern.
- Click the **Specify points** icon and click in the regions, as shown. Press ENTER and click **OK**.

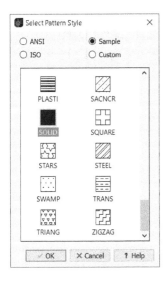

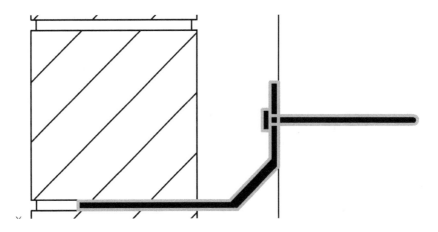

Creating the Insulation

- Click the **Offset** tool on the **Modify** panel of the **Home** ribbon tab. Next, type 1, and press ENTER.
- Select the vertical line, as shown. Next, move the pointer toward the right and click.
- Press ENTER twice. Next, type 9, and press ENTER.
- Select the offset line. Next, move the pointer toward the right and click.

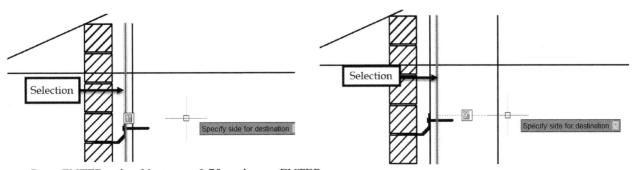

- Press ENTER twice. Next, type 0.75, and press ENTER.
- Select the offset line. Next, move the pointer toward the right and click.

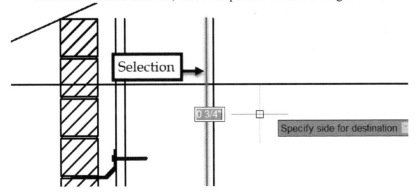

- Click the **Trim/Extend** drop-down > **Extend** on the **Modify** panel of the **Home** ribbon tab. Next, press ENTER.
- Click and drag a selection window across the ends of the vertical lines, as shown.
- Create the two horizontal lines, as shown.

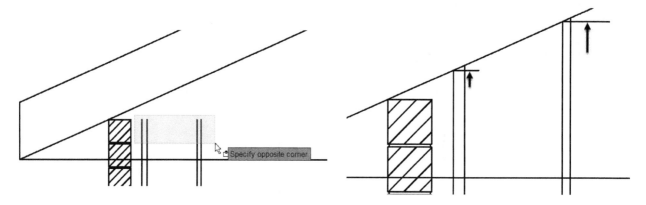

- Trim the extending portions.

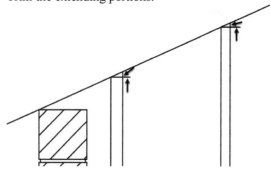

- Click the **Rectangle** drop-down > **Corner** on the **Draw** panel of the **Home** ribbon tab.
- Select the corner point, as shown.
- Right-click and select the **Dimensions** option. Next, type 9, and press ENTER.
- Type -2.25 and press ENTER.

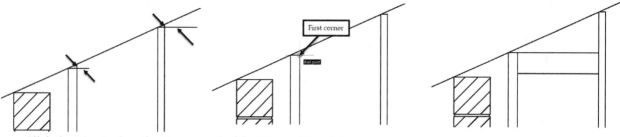

- Click the **Line** tool on the **Draw** panel of the **Home** ribbon tab.
- Create the diagonal lines by selecting the corner points of the rectangle.

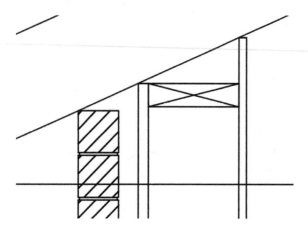

- Click **Circle** drop-down > **Circle Diameter** on the **Draw** panel on the **Home** ribbon tab.

- Select the midpoint of the left vertical edge of the rectangle. Next, type 1, and press ENTER.

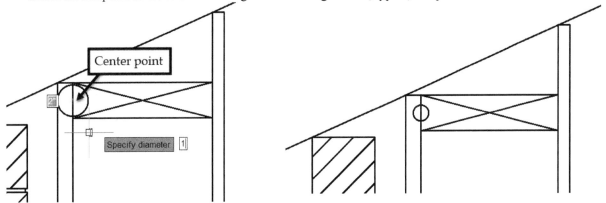

- Click the **Hatch** tool on the **Draw** panel of the **Home** ribbon tab.
- On the **Hatch /Fill** dialog, click the **Preview patterns** icon next to the **Pattern** drop-down,
- Select the **Sample** option from the **Select Pattern Style** dialog, and then select the **SOLID** pattern. Next, click **OK**.
- Click the **Specify entities** icon and select the circle, as shown. Press ENTER and click **OK**.

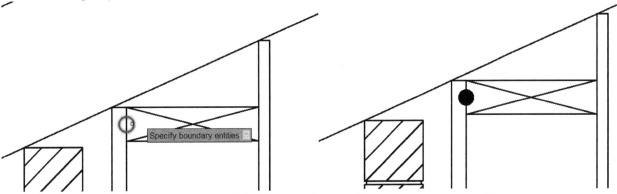

- Click the **Line** tool on the **Draw** panel of the **Home** ribbon tab. Next, create a horizontal line, as shown.
- Click the **Offset** tool on the **Modify** panel of the **Home** ribbon tab. Next, type 1.5, and press ENTER.
- Select the newly created line. Next, move the pointer downward and click.

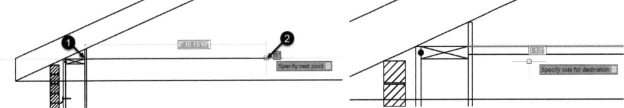

- Press ENTER twice. Next, type 0.75, and press ENTER.
- Select the offset line. Next, move the pointer downward and click.
- Click the **Trim** tool on the **Modify** panel of the **Home** ribbon tab.
- Trim the elements, as shown.

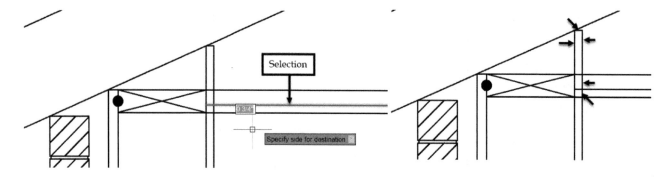

- Click the **Hatch** tool on the **Draw** panel of the **Home** ribbon tab.
- Type T in the command Bar and press Enter.
- On the **Hatch /Fill** dialog, click the **Preview patterns** ... icon next to the **Pattern** drop-down,
- Select the **ANSI** option from the **Select Pattern Style** dialog, and then select the **ANSI37** pattern. Next, click **OK**.
- Click the **Specify entities** icon and select the circle, as shown. Press ENTER and click **OK**.
- Type **2** in the **Scale** box. Next, type **45** in the **Angle** box.

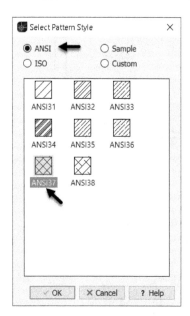

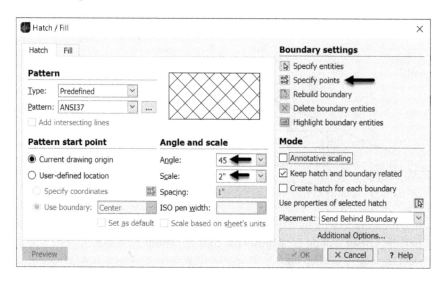

- Click the **Specify points** icon and click in the regions, as shown. Press ENTER and click **OK**.

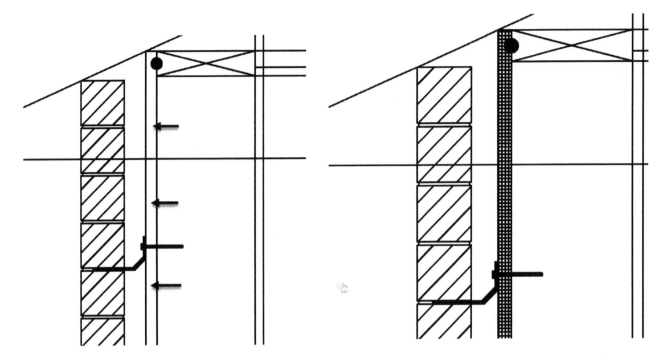

- Click the **Line** tool on the **Draw** panel of the **Home** ribbon tab.
- Select the midpoint of the horizontal line, as shown.
- Move the pointer downward and click. Next, press ESC.

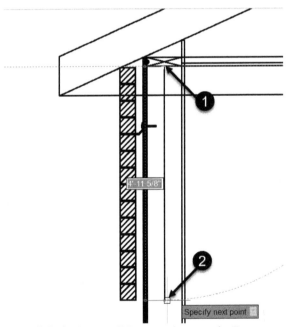

- Click the **Layers Manager** icon on the **Layers** panel of the **Home** ribbon tab.
- Click the **New Layer** icon on the **Layers Manager**. Next, type **Insulation** as the layer name.
- Click in the **LineStyle** column on the Layers Manager, and then select **Other**.

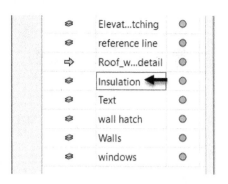
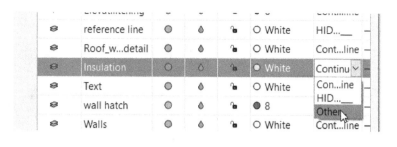

- Click the **Load** button on the **Line Style** dialog.
- Select the **BATTING** linestyle from the linestyle list on the **Load LineStyles** dialog. Next, click **OK**.
- Select the **BATTING** linestyle from the **Line Style** dialog. Next, click **OK**.

- Select the newly created line.
- Select **Insulation** from the **Layers Manager** drop-down on the **Layers** panel.

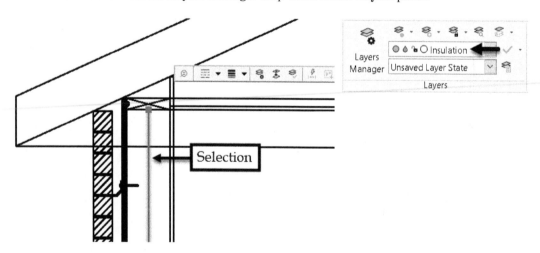

- Select the newly created line. Next, right-click and select **Properties**; the **Properties** palette appears on the right side of the graphics window.
- Type 10 in the **LineScale** box and press ENTER. Next, press ESC.

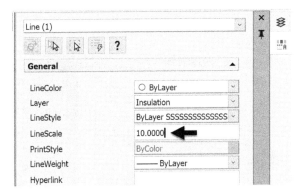

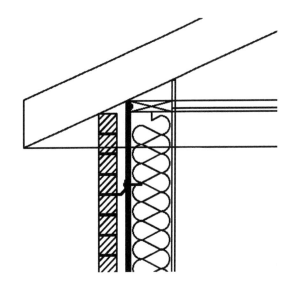

- Click the **Offset** tool on the **Modify** panel of the **Home** ribbon tab. Next, type 3, and press ENTER.
- Select the horizontal line, as shown. Next, move the pointer upward and click.

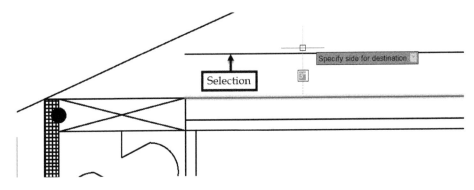

- Press ESC.
- Select the newly created line. Next, select **Insulation** from the **Layers Manager** drop-down on the **Layers** panel.
- Click the **Properties** tab on the graphics window. Next, type 6 in the **LineScale** box and press ENTER.
- Press ESC.

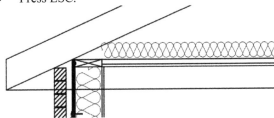

Creating the Roof Detail
- Offset the inclined line by 1". Next, close the end of the offset lines.

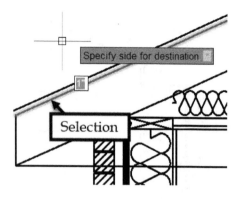
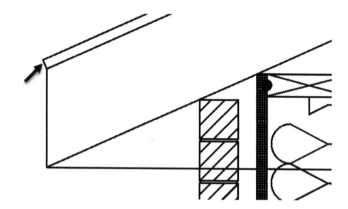

- Offset the new line by 0.5".
- Select the newly created offset line.
- Select HIDDENX2 from the **LineStyle Control** drop-down on the **Properties** panel.

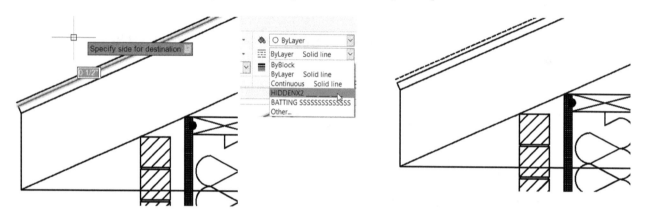

- Create another line with the offset distance of 0.75".
- On the **Modify** panel and click the **Fillet** drop-down > **Change Length** tool.
- Right-click and select the **Increment** option. Next, type 2.5, and press ENTER.
- Select the newly offset line.

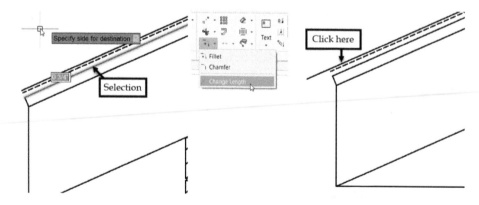

- Deactivate the **Ortho** button on the status bar.
- On the ribbon, click **View** tab > **Coordinates** panel > **CCS** icon.
- Select the endpoint of the inclined line, as shown. Next, select a point of the inclined, and then press ENTER.

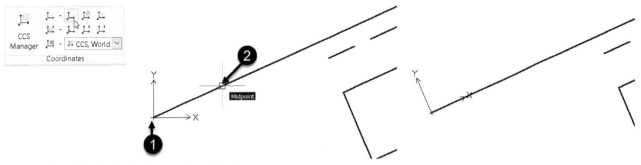

- Activate the **Ortho** button on the status bar.
- Click the **Line** tool on the **Draw** panel of the **Home** ribbon tab.
- Select the endpoint of the inclined line, as shown. Next, move the pointer downward.
- Type 0.25 and press ENTER. Next, move the pointer toward the right.
- Type 0.375, and press ENTER.

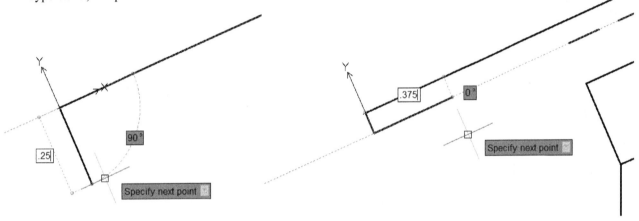

- On the ribbon, click **View** tab > **Coordinates** panel > **CCS, World** icon; the coordinate system is restored to its default location.

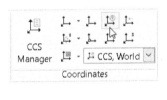

- Click the **Line** tool on the **Draw** panel of the **Home** ribbon tab. Next, select the endpoint of the last line.
- Move the pointer downward. Next, type 1.5, and press ENTER.
- Type @.375<225 in the command window and press ENTER.
- Press Esc.

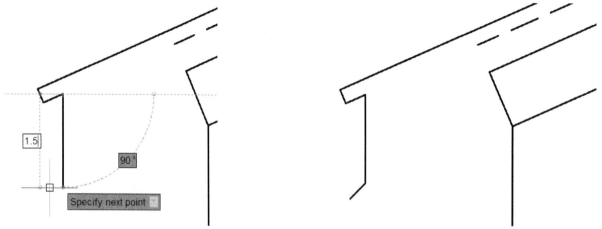

- On the **Draw** panel, click **Arc** drop-down > **Start, Center, End**. Next, select the endpoint of the line, as shown.
- Select the centerpoint of the line. Next, select the other endpoint of the line, as shown
- Delete the line between the endpoints of the arc.

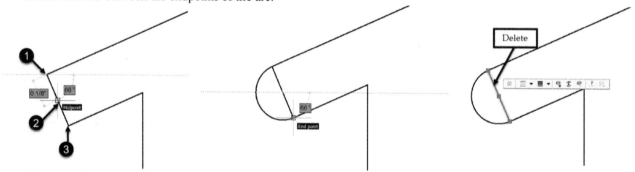

- On the ribbon, click Home tab > **Modify** panel > **Weld** drop-down > **Split at point**. Next, select the inclined line.
- Press and hold the SHIFT key, and then right click. Next, select the **From** option from the shortcut menu.
- Select the endpoint of the selected line. Next, move the pointer on the selected line.
- Type 9 and press ENTER; the line is broken at the specified distance.

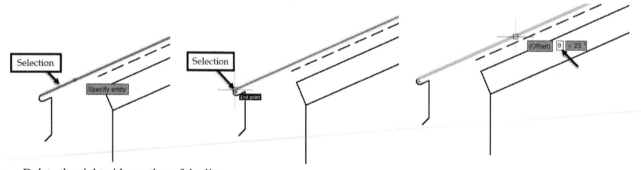

- Delete the right-side portion of the line.

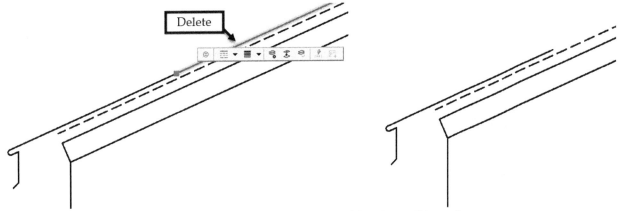

- Click the **Rectangle** drop-down > **Corner** on the **Draw** panel of the **Home** ribbon tab.
- Select the corner point, as shown. Next, right-click and select the **Dimensions** option.
- Type -1 and press ENTER. Next, type -10 and press ENTER.

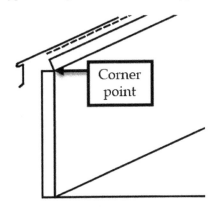

- Click the **Rectangle** > **Corner** on the **Draw** panel of the **Home** ribbon tab.
- Select the top-left corner of the rectangle, as shown. Next, right-click and select the **Dimensions** option.
- Type -1 and press ENTER. Next, type -2.5 and press ENTER.
- Move the newly created rectangle downward by 0.5".

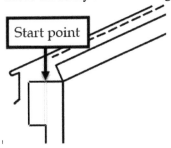
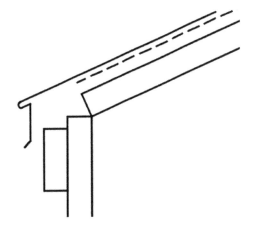

- Click the **Trim/Extend** drop-down > **Trim** on the **Modify** panel of the **Home** ribbon tab.
- Select the vertical edge of the brick, as shown. Next, press ENTER.
- Click on the horizontal line on the right side.

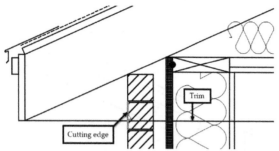

- Click the **Offset** tool on the **Modify** panel of the **Home** ribbon tab. Next, type 1, and press ENTER.
- Select the horizontal line trimmed in the last step.
- Move the pointer upward and click.
- Select the offset line. Next, move the pointer upward and click.

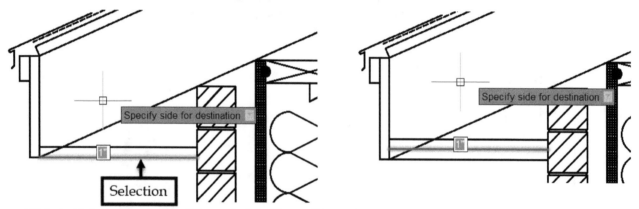

- Click the **Trim** tool on the **Modify** panel of the **Home** ribbon tab. Next, press ENTER.
- Select the portions of the lines, as shown.

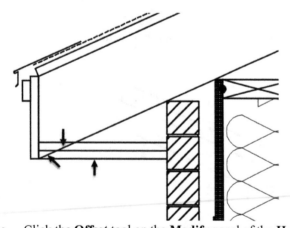

- Click the **Offset** tool on the **Modify** panel of the **Home** ribbon tab. Next, type 7, and press ENTER.
- Select the left vertical line of the veneer brick. Next, move the pointer toward the left and click.
- Press ENTER twice.
- Type 4 and press ENTER. Next, select the offset line.
- Move the pointer toward the left and click.

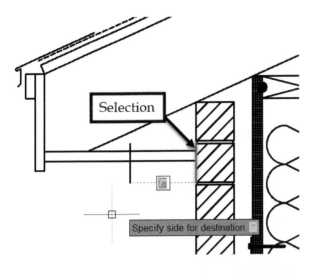

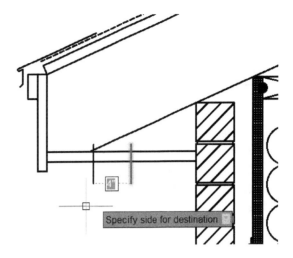

- Click the **Trim** tool on the **Modify** panel of the **Home** ribbon tab.
- Select the portions of the lines, as shown.
- Create a line by selecting the corner points of the opening, as shown.

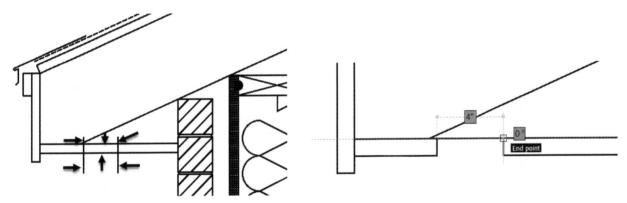

- Press ESC.
- Activate the **Ortho** icon on the status bar.
- Select the newly created line and click **Copy** drop-down > **Scale** on the **Modify** panel of the **Home** ribbon tab.
- Select the midpoint. Next, move the pointer vertically downward.
- Type 1.25 as the scale factor, and then press ENTER.

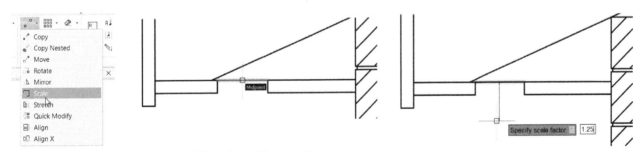

- Select the horizontal line and click on its midpoint grip.
- Move the pointer upward. Next, type 0.2, and press ENTER.
- Create an inclined line and pattern it, as shown.

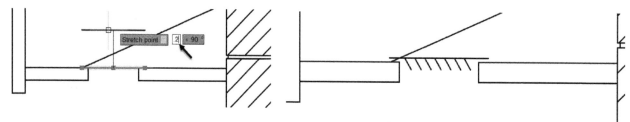

- On the **Home** tab of the ribbon, click **Draw** panel > **Hatch** drop-down > **Hatch**.
- Type **T** on the command bar and press Enter.
- On the **Hatch /Fill** dialog, click the **Preview patterns** [...] icon next to the **Pattern** drop-down,
- Select the **Sample** option from the **Select Pattern Style** dialog, and then select the **DASH** pattern.
- Click **OK** on the **Select Pattern Style** dialog.
- Click the **Specify points** icon under the **Boundary settings** section.
- Pick points in the areas, as shown. Next, press ENTER.

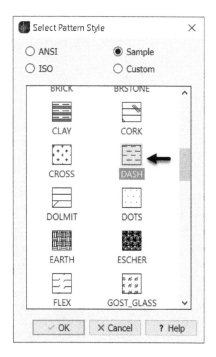

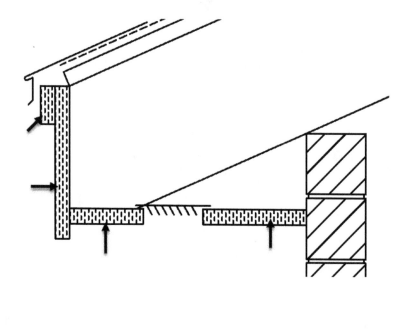

- Type **90** and **2** in the **Angle** and **Scale** boxes, respectively. Next, click **OK**.
- On the **Home** tab of the ribbon, click **Draw** panel > **Rectangle** drop-down > **Corner**.
- Select the lower right corner of the rectangle, as shown. Next, right-click and select the **Dimensions** option.
- Type **-6** and press ENTER. Next, type **-5** and press ENTER.

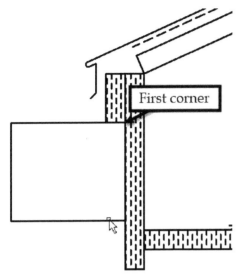

- Select the rectangle and click the **Copy** drop-down > **Move** tool on the **Modify** panel.
- Select the top right corner point of the rectangle.
- Move the pointer downward. Next, type 0.5, and press ENTER.
- Select the rectangle and click the **Move** tool on the **Modify** panel.
- Select the top right corner point of the rectangle.
- Move the pointer toward left. Next, type 0.25, and press ENTER.

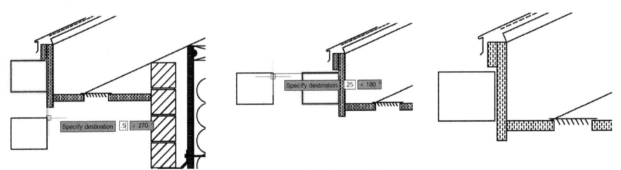

- Click **Circle** drop-down > **Center** on the **Draw** panel of the **Home** ribbon tab.
- Select the lower-left corner of the rectangle.
- Type 8 and press ENTER.
- Select the circle. Next, click on the centerpoint of the circle.
- Move the pointer toward left. Next, type 7, and press ENTER.

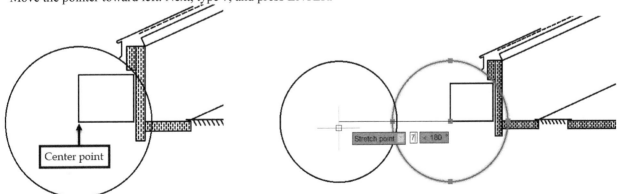

- Click the **Trim/Extend** drop-down **> Trim** on the **Modify** panel. Next, press ENTER.
- Trim the edges of the circle and rectangle, as shown.

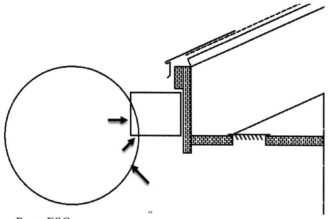 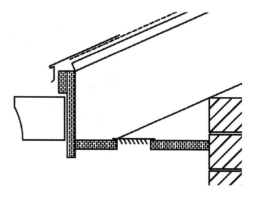

- Press ESC.
- Select the rectangle and click the **Explode** tool on the **Modify** panel.

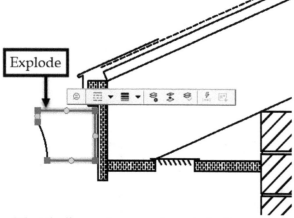

- Select the lines and arcs, as shown in the figure.
- On the **Home** ribbon tab, click the **LineWeight Control** drop-down on the **Properties** panel, and then select 0.70.

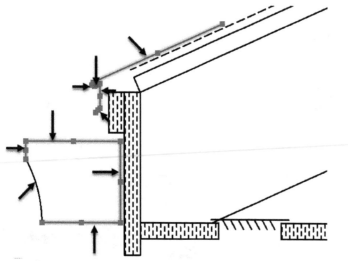

- Press Esc.
- Click the **Offset** tool on the **Modify** panel. Next, type 1.25, and press ENTER.
- Select the offset line, as shown in the figure. Next, move the pointer upward and click.

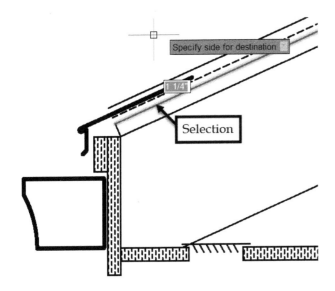

- Deactivate the **Ortho** button on the status bar.
- On the ribbon, click **View** tab > **Coordinates** panel > **CCS** icon.
- Select the endpoint of the inclined line, as shown. Next, select a point of the inclined, and then press ENTER.

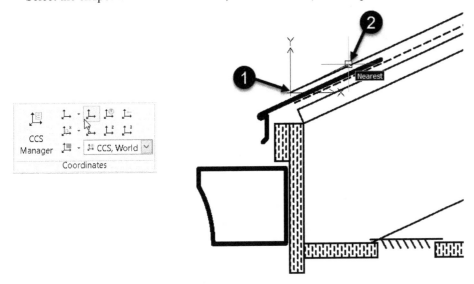

- Activate the **Ortho** button on the status bar.
- Click the **Line** tool on the **Draw** panel of the **Home** ribbon tab.
- Select the endpoint of the offset line. Move the pointer upward.
- Type 2 and press ENTER.
- Type @7<355 in the command window and press ENTER.

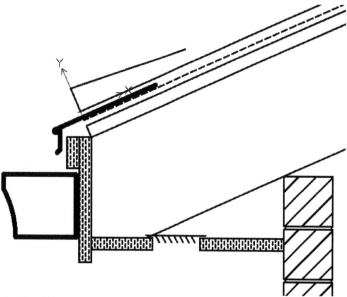

- On the ribbon, click **View** tab > **Coordinates** panel > **CCS, World** icon; the coordinate system is restored to its default location.
- Select the two newly created lines.
- Click the **Pattern** tool on the **Modify** panel.
- Click the **Specify path** icon on the **Pattern** dialog. Next, select the offset to define the path.
- Select the **Measure Equally** option from the **Base pattern on** drop-down.
- Type **10** in the **Between** box. Next, click **OK**.

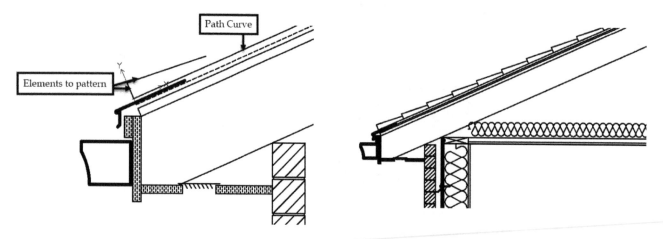

Adding Annotations

- On the **Home** ribbon tab, click **Leader** drop-down > **Insert** on the **Annotations** panel.
- Deactivate the **Ortho** button on the status bar.
- Specify the start point of the leader on the insulation, as shown.
- Move the pointer diagonally toward the bottom right corner, and then click.

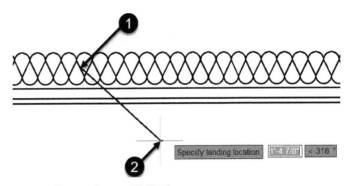

- Type 2 in the **Text Height** box on the **Note Formatting** toolbar and press ENTER.

- Type **Insulation** and click in the graphics area.

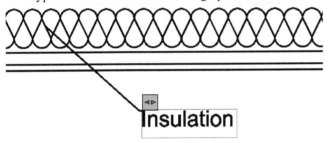

- Select the leader. Next, right-click and select the **Properties** option.
- On the **Properties** palette, scroll to the **Leaders** section and enter 2 in the **Arrow size** and **Landing distance** boxes, respectively.
- Scroll to the **Text** section, and then **1** in the **Landing gap** box.

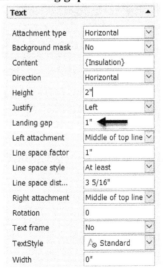

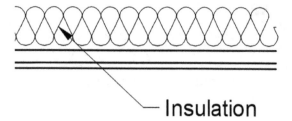

Insulation

- On the **Home** ribbon tab, click **Leader** drop-down > **Insert** on the **Annotation** panel.
- Specify the start point of the leader on the circle, as shown.
- Move the pointer diagonally toward the bottom right corner, and then click.
- Type **Continuous Bead of Sealant** and click in the graphics area.
- Click the **Properties Painter** tool on the **Properties** panel.

- Select the **Insulation** leader to specify the source object.
- Select the newly created leader; the properties of the source object are matched with the destination object.

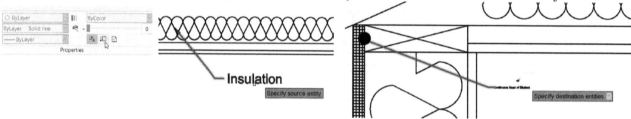

- Likewise, create the remaining leaders, as shown.

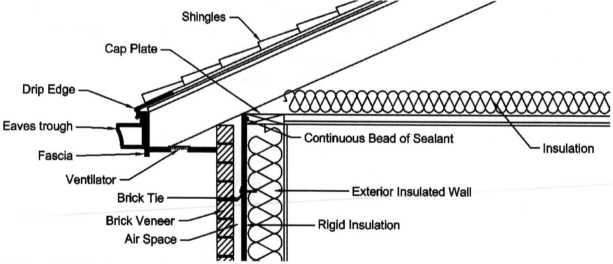

- Activate the **Ortho** button on the status bar.
- On the ribbon, click the **Home** tab > **Draw > Rectangle** drop-down > **Corner**.
- Click in the empty area. Next, right-click and select **Dimensions**.
- Type 6 and press ENTER. Next, type 12, and press ENTER.
- Press ENTER and select the top-right corner of the rectangle. Next, right-click and select **Dimensions**.
- Type 2 and press ENTER. Next, type -5 and press ENTER.
- Press ENTER and select the bottom-left corner of the large rectangle. Next, right-click and select **Dimensions**.
- Type -2 and press ENTER. Next, type 5, and press ENTER.

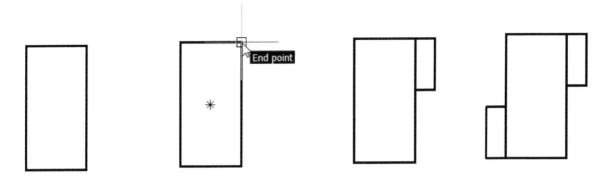

- Type L in the command window and press ENTER.
- Select the corner points of the rectangle in the sequence, as shown.

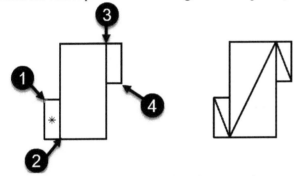

- Create two horizontal lines and delete the rectangles.

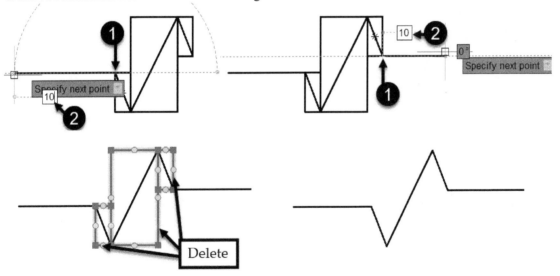

- Create a selection window across all the elements of the break line.
- Type CO and press ENTER. Next, select the left endpoint of the breakpoint.
- Move the pointer toward the wall detail and select the point, as shown. Next, press ESC.

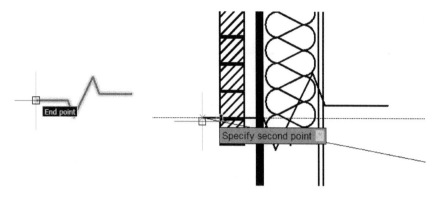

- On the **Home** ribbon tab, click **Trim** drop-down > **Trim** on the **Modify** panel.
- Select the elements of the break line and press ENTER.
- Trim the elements on the bottom side of the drawing.

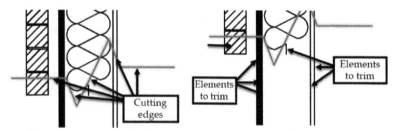 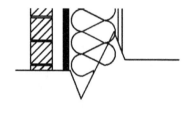

- Likewise, create the break lines and trim the elements, as shown.

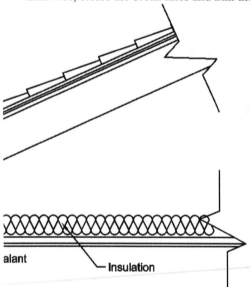

- Save and close the drawing file.

Tutorial 6: Sheets and Title Block

- Open the Tutorial 1 drawing file.
- Click the **Sheet 1** tab at the bottom of the graphics window.

Notice that a white paper is displayed with a viewport created automatically. The components of a sheet are shown in the figure below.

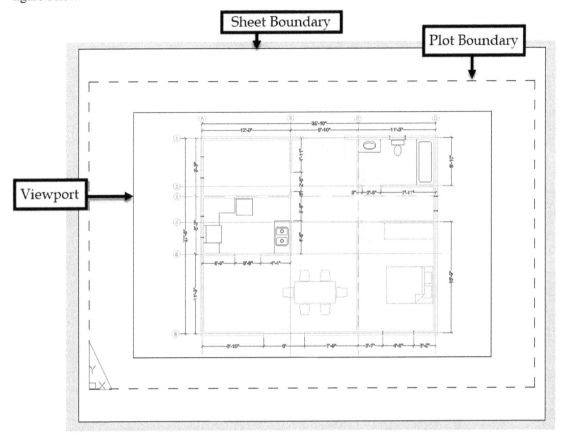

- Click **Sheets > Sheets > Print Configuration Manager** on the ribbon; the **Print Configuration Manager** dialog appears. On the **Print Configuration Manager** dialog, click the **New** button; the **New Print Configuration** dialog appears.

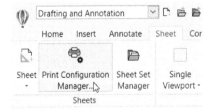
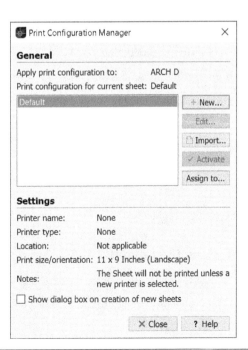

- Select the **Default** option from the **New Print Configuration** dialog, and then click **OK**.

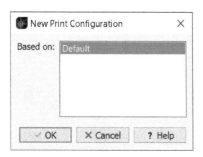

- On the **Save Print Configuration** dialog, type **ARCH D** in the **File name** box. Next, click **Save.**
- On the **Print Configuration** dialog, select **PDF** from the **Name** drop-down under the **Printer/Plotter** group.
- Set the **Paper size** to **ARCH D (36.00 x 24.00 inches)**. Next, uncheck the **Fit to paper size** option and set the **Scale** to **1:1**.
- Set the **PlotStyle table** to **default.ctb**.

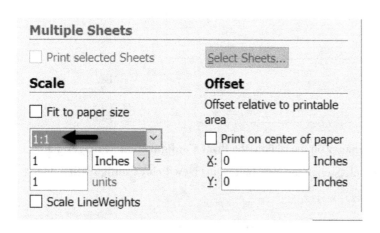

- Click **Save** on the **Print Configuration** dialog.
- Select the **ARCH D** print configuration, and then click the **Activate** button.
- Click **Close** on the **Print Configuration Manager** dialog.
- Double-click on the **Sheet1** tab and enter **ARCH D**; the **Sheet1** is renamed.

Creating the Title Block on the Layout

You can draw objects on layouts to create title blocks, borders, and viewports. However, it is not recommended to draw the actual drawing on layouts. You can also create dimensions on layouts.

- Click the **ARCH D** sheet tab.
- Create the **Title Block** layer and make it current. Select the viewport on the sheet and press Delete.

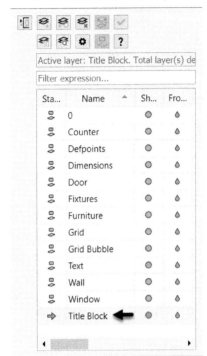

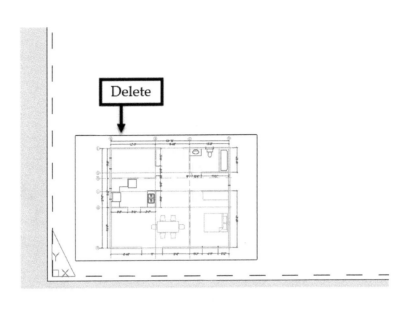

- Create the border and title block, as shown. Insert text inside the title block, as shown.

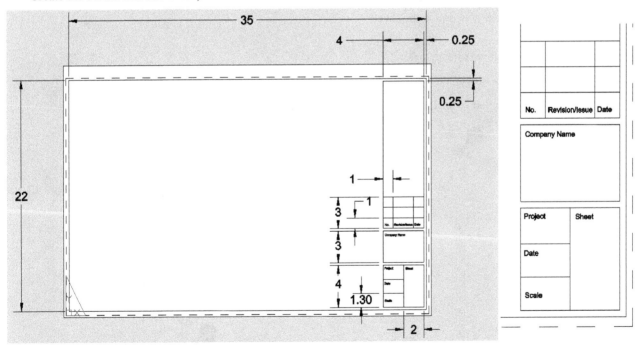

- On the ribbon, click **Insert > Block > Define**. Next, type **Title Block** in the **Name** box of **Block Definition** dialog.
- Click the **Select in graphics area** icon under the **Entities** section. Next, select the elements of the title block, and then press ENTER.
- Click the **Select in graphics area** icon under the **Base point** section. Next, select the lower right corner point of the title block, and then press ENTER.

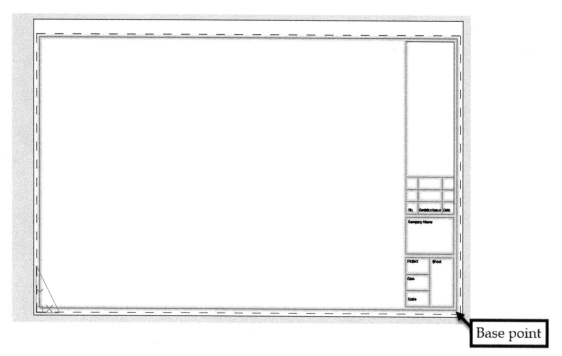

- Select the **Convert to block** option from the **Entities** section, and then click **OK**.

Creating Viewports in the Paper space

The viewports that exist in the paper space are called floating viewports. Because you can position them anywhere in the sheet, and modify their shape size concerning the sheet.

- Open the **ARCH D** sheet, if not already open.
- Click **Sheet > Viewports > Single Viewport** on the ribbon.
- Create the rectangular viewport by picking the first and second corner points, as shown in the figure.

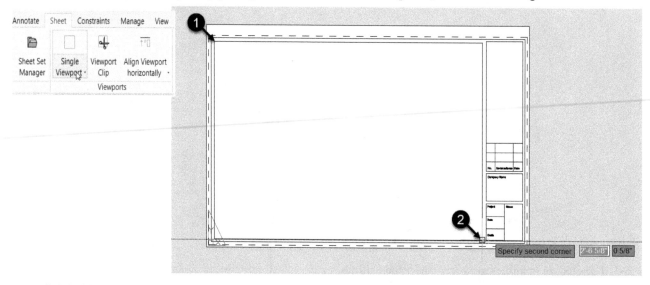

- Click inside the viewport; the model space inside the viewport is activated. Also, the viewport frame becomes thicker when you are in model space.
- Click the **Annotation** drop-down and select **1:30** from the menu; the drawing is zoomed out.

- Click in the area outside the viewport to switch back to paper space.

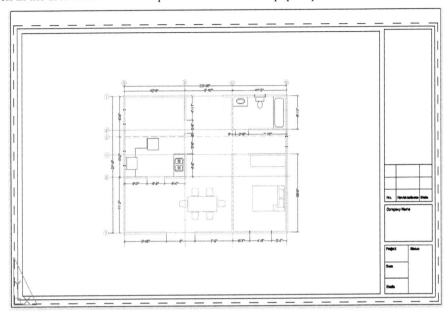

To hide viewport frames while plotting a drawing, follow the steps given below.

- Click the **Layers Manager** tab on the right side of the graphics area.

- In the **Layers Manager**, create a new layer called **Hide Viewports** and make it current.

- Deactivate the plotter symbol 🖨 under the **Print** column of the **Hide Viewports** layer; the object on this layer will not be print. Close the **Layers Manager**.

- On the ribbon, click **Home** tab > **Layers** panel > **Active Layer** drop-down > **Entity to Active Layer** button.

- Select the viewport in the **ARCH D** sheet and press ENTER; the viewport frames are unplottable.

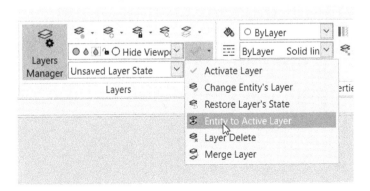

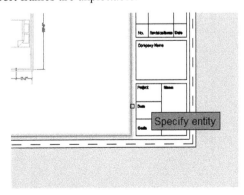

- Save the drawing file.

Tutorial 7: Printing

- Open the Tutorial 1 file.
- On the Application Menu, click **Print > Print**.
- Select the **default.ctb** option from the **PrintStyle table** section, and then click the **Edit** button.
- On the **Plot Style Table Editor** dialog, select **Color 1** from the **Print styles** list. Next, set the **LineWeight** to 0.1000 mm. Likewise, change the lineweights of the other colors, as shown.

Color	Lineweight
Color 1	0.1 mm
Color 2	0.2 mm
Color 3	1.0 mm
Color 4	0.5 mm
Color 5	0.7 mm
Color 6	0.5 mm
Color 8	0.09 mm
Color 9	0.05 mm

- Press and hold the Shift key and select Color 1 and Color 9. Set **LineColor** to **Black**. Click **OK** on the **Plot Style Table Editor** dialog.
- Click **OK** on the **Additional Options** dialog.
- On the **Print** dialog, click **Print Preview**; the print preview of the drawing appears.
- Click **Close** on the top right corner.

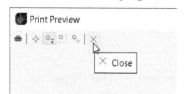

- Click **OK** to print the drawing.
- Save and close the drawing.

Exercise

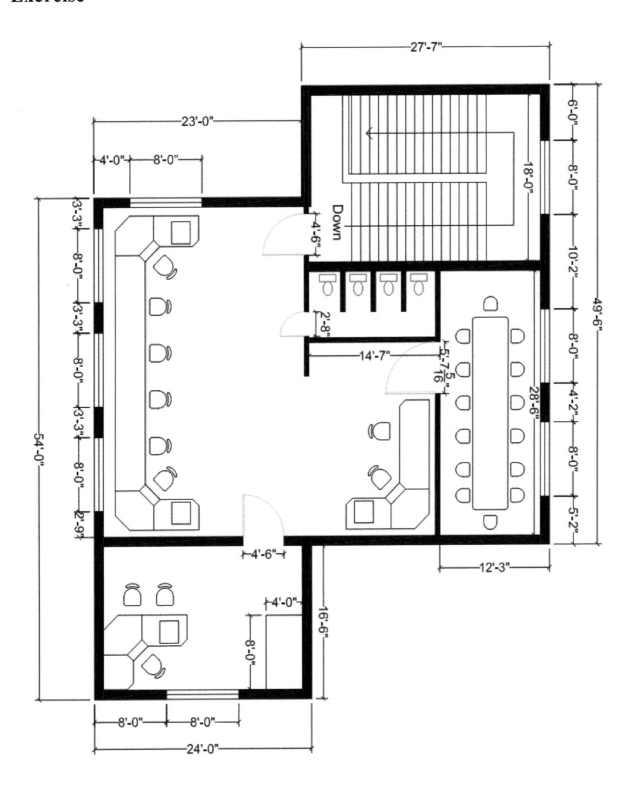

Tutorial 8

In this example, you will learn to create drawing shown in figure.

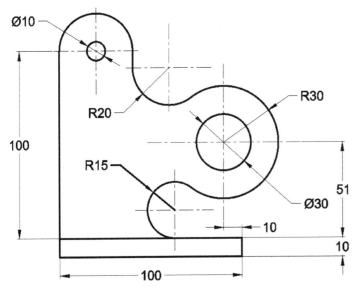

- Double-click on the **CoralCAD** icon on your desktop.

- Set the **Workspace** to **Drafting and Annotation**.

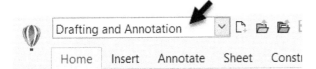

- Type **UNITSYSTEM** in the command window and press Enter.

- On the **Unit System** page, select **Type > Decimal** from the **Length** section. Next, select **Precision > 0.000**.

- Select **Millimeters** from the **Block units format** drop-down in the **Unit Scale** section. Next, click **OK**.

- Type DRAWINGBOUNDS in the command window and press Enter.

- Press Enter to accept 0, 0 as the lower limit.

- Type 420, 297 in the command window, and press Enter. The program sets the upper limit of the drawing.

- Make sure that the **Grid** icon is turned OFF on the status bar.

- On the ribbon, click **View > Navigate > Zoom Extents** drop-down > **Zoom Bounds**.

- On the Status bar, turn ON the **Ortho** icon.

- On the ribbon, click **Home > Draw > Rectangle**. Next, click at an arbitrary location.

- Right click and select **Dimensions** from the shortcut menu.

- Type-in 100 and press Enter. It defines the horizontal distance of the rectangle.

- Type-in 10 and press Enter. It defines the vertical distance of the rectangle.

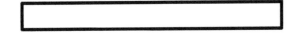

- Click the **Polyline** tool on the **Draw** panel of the **Home** ribbon tab.
- Select the top left corner of the rectangle. Next, move the pointer up.
- Type 100 and press ENTER.
- Type A in the command window and press ENTER.
- Move the pointer toward right. Next, type 40 and press ENTER.
- Move the pointer downward up to a random distance and click. Next, press ESC.

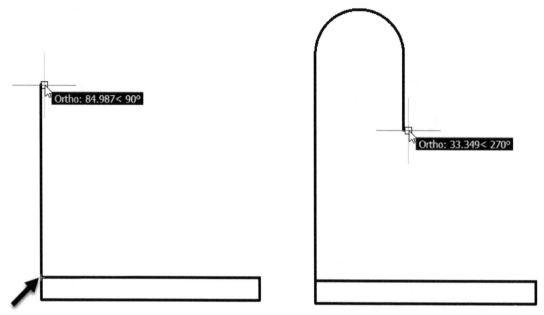

- On the **Home** ribbon tab, click **Draw** panel > **Line** drop-down > **Infinite Line** tool.
- Right click and select the **Offset** option from the shortcut menu.
- Type **10** and press ENTER. Next, select the right vertical line.
- Click on the left side of the selected line; a vertical infinite line is created.

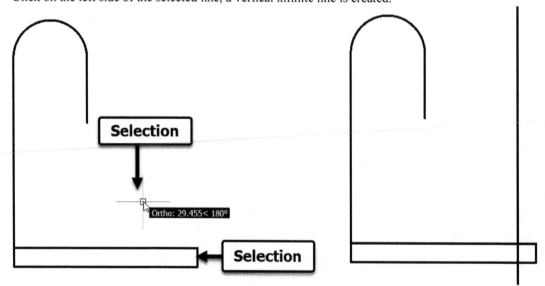

- Press ENTER twice. Next, type O and press ENTER.
- Type **51** and press ENTER.
- Select the top horizontal line of the rectangle, as shown.
- Move the pointer upward and click.

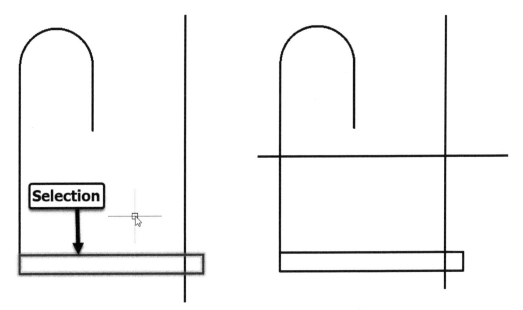

- Click **Circle** drop-down > **Circle** on the **Draw** panel on the **Home** ribbon tab.
- Select the intersection point of the vertical and horizontal infinite line. Next, type 30, and press ENTER.

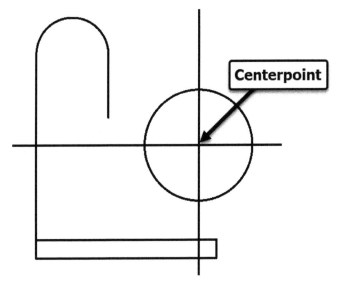

- On the ribbon, click **Home > Draw > Circle drop-down > Tangent, Tangent, Radius**.
- Select the vertical line and the circle, as shown.
- Type 20 and press ENTER.

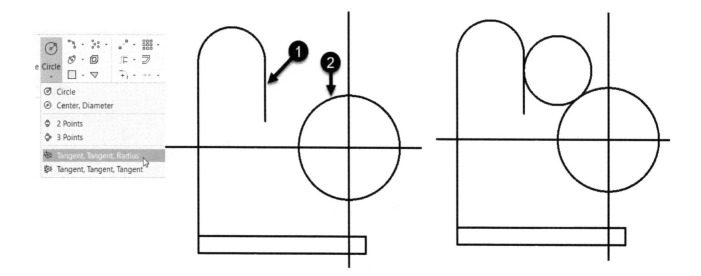

- On the ribbon, click **Home > Draw > Circle drop-down > Tangent, Tangent, Radius**.

- Select the circle and the horizontal line of the rectangle, as shown.

- Type 15 and press ENTER.

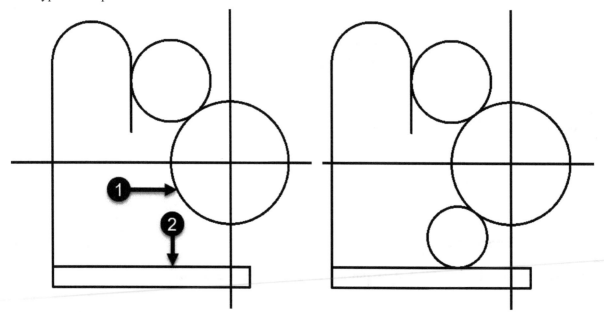

- Click **Home** tab > **Modify** panel > **Trim/Extend** drop-down > **Power Trim** on the ribbon.

- Press and hold the left mouse button and drag it across the entities, as shown below. Press ESC.

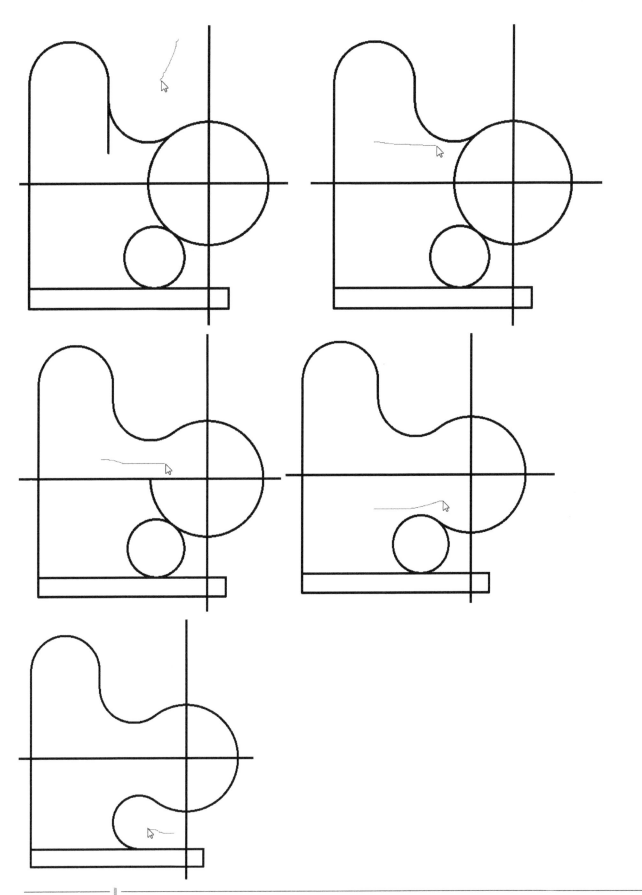

- Select the two infinite lines. Right-click and select **Delete**.

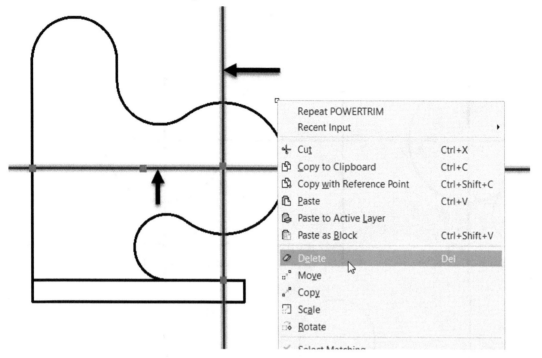

- On the ribbon, click **Home** tab > **Draw** panel > **Circle** drop-down > **Center, Diameter**.

- Select the center point of the large arc. Move the pointer outward, type 30 and press ENTER.

- Select the center point of the top arc. Move the pointer outward, type 10 and press ENTER.

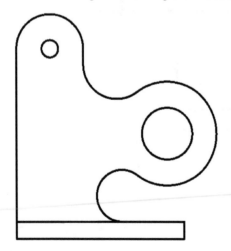

Tutorial 9

In this example, you will learn to create drawing shown in figure.

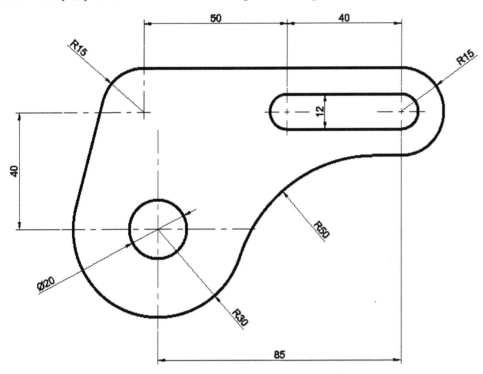

- Double-click on the **CoralCAD** icon on your desktop.
- Set the **Workspace** to **Drafting and Annotation**.
- On the ribbon, click **Home > Draw > Rectangle**. Next, click at an arbitrary location.
- Right click and select **Dimensions** from the shortcut menu.
- Type-in 90 and press Enter. It defines the horizontal distance of the rectangle.
- Type-in 30 and press Enter. It defines the vertical distance of the rectangle.

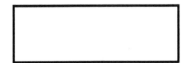

- Click **Circle** drop-down > **2 Points** on the **Draw** panel on the **Home** ribbon tab.
- Select the top-left and bottom-left corners of the rectangle.
- Click **Circle** drop-down > **2 Points** on the **Draw** panel on the **Home** ribbon tab.
- Select the top-right and bottom-right corners of the rectangle.

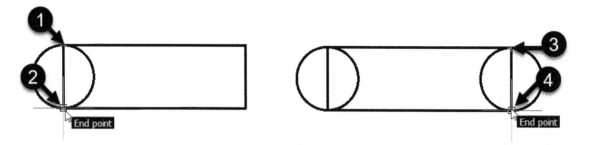

- Click **Home** tab > **Modify** panel > **Trim/Extend** drop-down > **Power Trim** on the ribbon.
- Press and hold the left mouse button and drag it across the entities, as shown below. Press ESC.

- On the ribbon, click **Home** > **Modify** > **Offset**. Next, type-in 9 in the command window and press Enter.
- Select the right arc of the slot. Next, click inside the slot.
- Likewise, offset the other entities, as shown below.

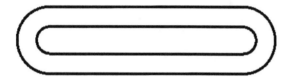

- On the ribbon, click **Home** > **Modify** > **Copy** drop-down > **Stretch**.
- Click and drag a selection window from the midpoint of the inner slot. Next, release the pointer outside the left arc of the inner slot.

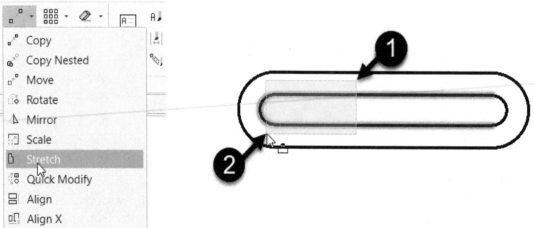

- Press ENTER. Next, place the pointer of the left arc, and then select its center point.
- Click the **Ortho** icon on the Status bar.
- Move the pointer horizontally toward right. Type 50 and press ENTER.

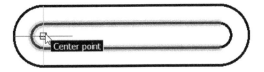
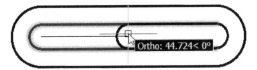

- On the **Home** ribbon tab, click **Draw** panel > **Line** drop-down > **Infinite Line** tool.
- Right click and select the **Vertical** option from the shortcut menu.
- Select the centerpoint of the right arc of the slot.
- Press ENTER twice.
- Right click and select the **Offset** option from the shortcut menu.
- Type 85 as the offset distance. Next, press ENTER.
- Select the newly created infinite line. Next, move the pointer toward the left and click.

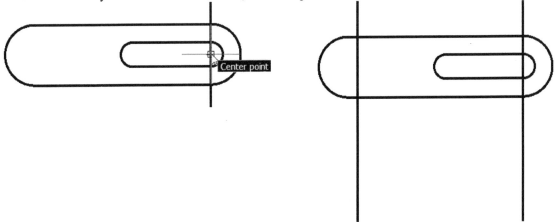

- Press ENTER twice.
- Right click and select the **Offset** option from the shortcut menu.
- Type 25 as the offset distance. Next, press ENTER.
- Select the lower horizontal line of the outer slot. Next, move the pointer downward and click.

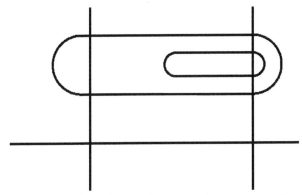

- Click **Circle** drop-down > **Circle** on the **Draw** panel on the **Home** ribbon tab.
- Select the intersection point of the vertical and horizontal infinite line. Next, type 30, and press ENTER.
- Again, select the intersection point of the vertical and horizontal infinite lines.
- Type 10 and press ENTER.

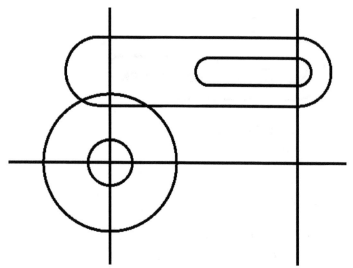

- Select all the infinite lines and press DELETE.

- On the ribbon, click **Home > Draw > Circle** drop-down **> Tangent, Tangent, Radius**.

- Select the horizontal line and the circle, as shown.

- Type 50 and press ENTER.

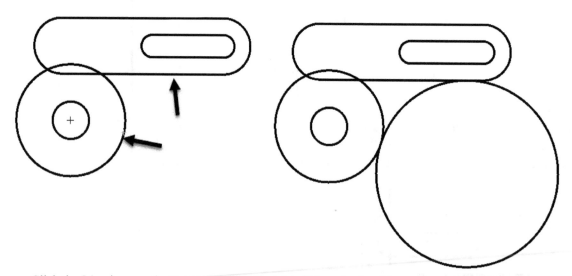

- Click the **Line** icon on the **Draw** panel. Next, right-click and select **Esnap Overrides > Tangent**.

- Select the left arc of the large slot.

- Right-click and select **Esnap Overrides > Tangent**. Next, click on the left side of the large circle.

- Press ESC.

- Trim the unwanted portions, as shown.

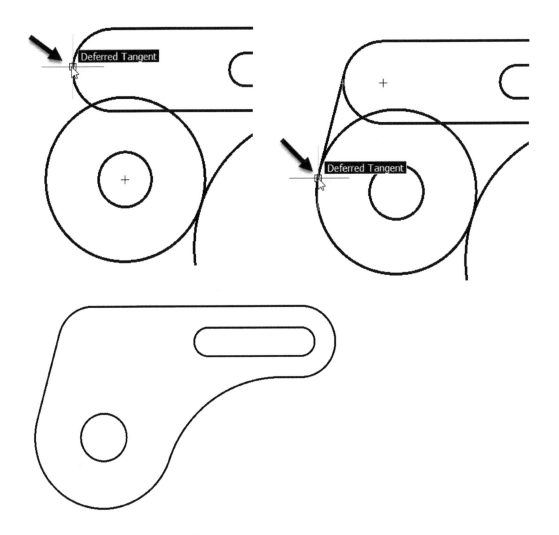

- Save and close the drawing file.

Tutorial 10

In this example, you will learn to create drawing shown in figure.

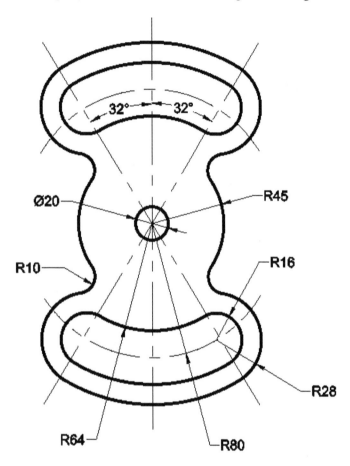

- Double-click on the **CoralCAD** icon on your desktop.

- Set the **Workspace** to **Drafting and Annotation**.

- On the **Home** ribbon tab, click **Draw** panel > **Line** drop-down > **Infinite Line** tool.
- Right click and select the **Angle** option from the shortcut menu.
- Type **120** and press ENTER. Next, click in the graphics window to place the infinite line.
- Press ENTER twice. Next, type **A** in the command window and press ENTER.
- Type 60 and press ENTER. Next, click in the graphics window.

- On the ribbon, click **Home** tab > **Draw** panel > **Circle** drop-down > **Center, Diameter**.

- Select the intersection point of the two infinite lines. Next, type 20, and press ENTER.

- Likewise, create six more circles, as shown.

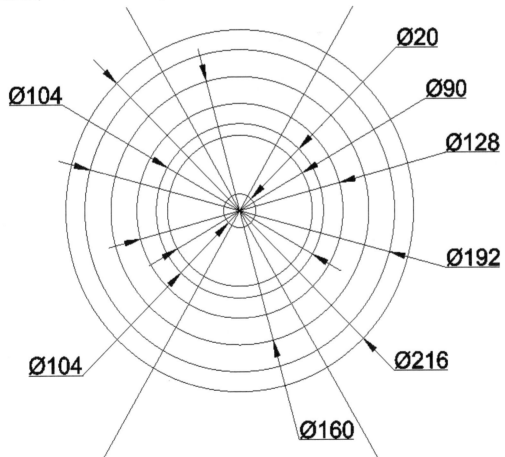

- Click **Home** tab > **Modify** panel > **Trim/Extend** drop-down > **Power Trim** on the ribbon.

- Press and hold the left mouse button and drag it across the entities, as shown below. Press ESC.

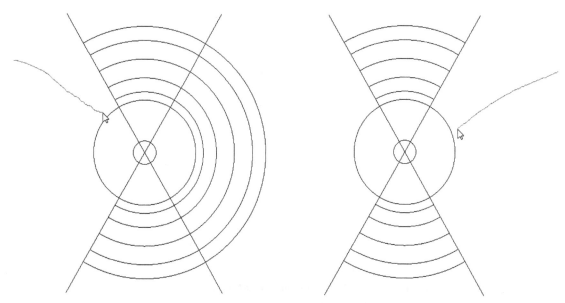

- On the ribbon, click **Home > Draw > Arc drop-down > Start, Center, End**.

- Specify the start, center, and end points of the arc.

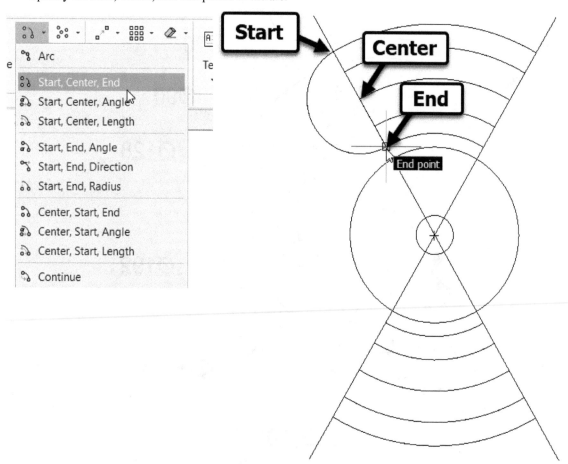

- Likewise, create another arc using the **Start, Center, End** command.

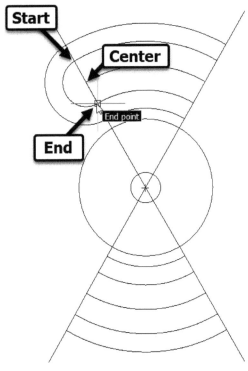

- On the ribbon, click **Home > Modify > Copy** drop-down > **Mirror**, and then select the two newly created arcs. Press Enter to accept the selection.

- Click the **Ortho** icon on the Status bar.

- Select the center point of the circle located at the center. Next, move the pointer upward and click.

- Select **No** to keep the original objects.

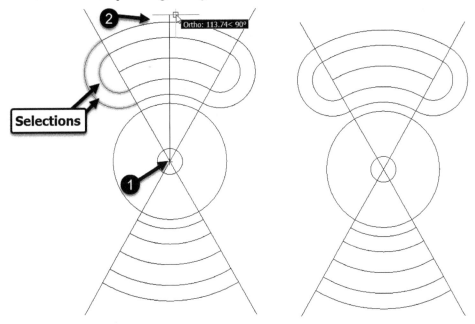

- On the ribbon, click **Home > Modify > Copy** drop-down > **Mirror**, and then select the two newly created arcs. Press Enter to accept the selection.

- Click the **Ortho** icon on the Status bar.

- Select the center point of the circle located at the center. Next, move the pointer toward right and click.

- Select **No** to keep the original objects.

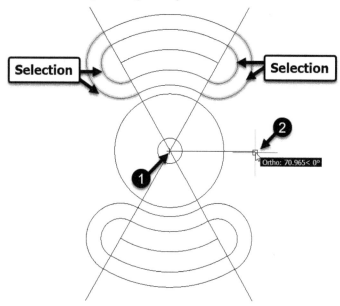

- On the ribbon, click **Home > Draw > Circle drop-down > Tangent, Tangent, Radius**.

- Select the arc and the circle, as shown. Next, type 10 and press ENTER.

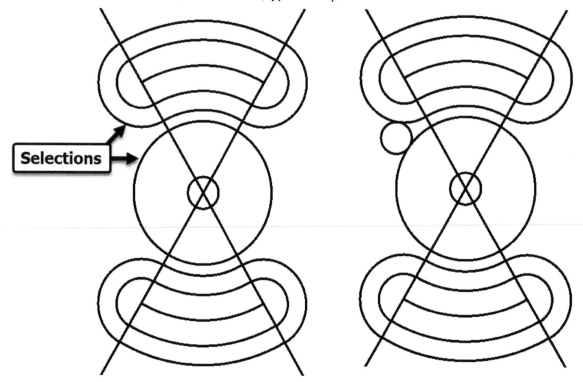

- Likewise, create three more circles using the **Tangent, Tangent, Radius** tool.

- Click **Home** tab > **Modify** panel > **Trim/Extend** drop-down > **Power Trim** on the ribbon.

- Press and hold the left mouse button and drag it across the entities, as shown below. Press ESC.

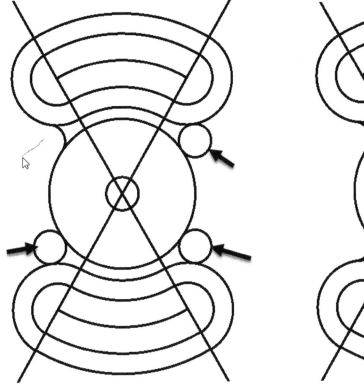

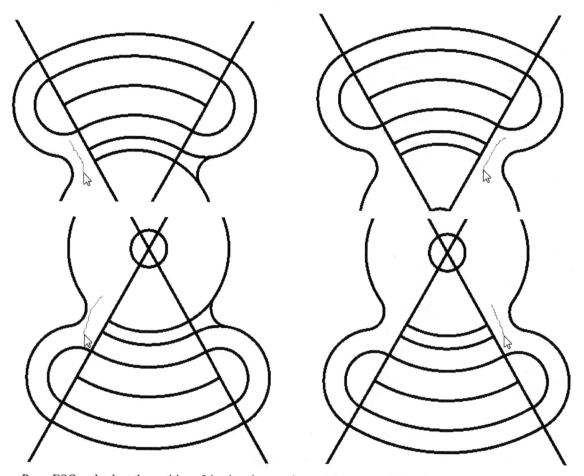

- Press ESC and select the entities of the drawing, as shown. Next, press DELETE..

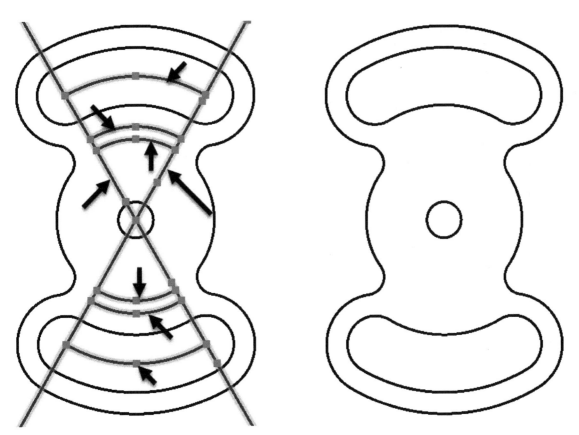

- Save and close the drawing file.

Tutorial 11

In this example, you will create the drawing shown in the figure.

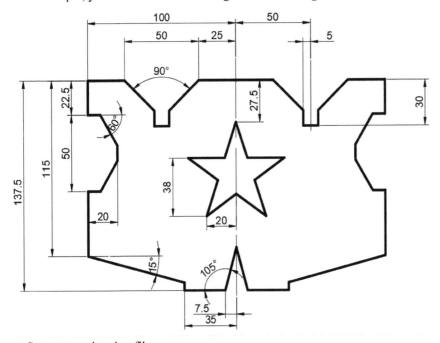

- Start a new drawing file.

- Activate the **Ortho** icon on the Status bar.
- On the **Draw** panel, click **Line** drop-down > **Line**. Next, pick a point in the graphics area.

- Move the pointer toward the right and type 35 and press ENTER.
- Move the pointer upward. Type 22.5 and press ENTER.
- Move the pointer toward the right. Type 65 and press ENTER.
- Move the pointer upward. Type 42.5 and press ENTER.
- Move the pointer toward left. Type 20 and press ENTER.
- Move the pointer upward. Type 50 and press ENTER.
- Move the pointer toward the right. Type 20 and press ENTER.
- Move the pointer upward. Type 22.5 and press ENTER.
- Move the pointer toward left. Type 45 and press ENTER.
- Move the pointer downward. Type 30 and press ENTER.
- Move the pointer toward left. Type 10 and press ENTER.
- Move the pointer upward. Type 30 and press ENTER.
- Move the pointer toward left. Type 45 and press ENTER.
- Move the pointer downward and select the start point of the drawing.

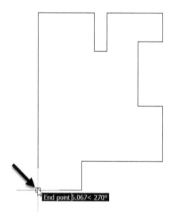

- Press ESC.

- On the ribbon, click **Home** tab > **Modify** panel > **Fillet** drop-down > **Chamfer**.

- Right-click and select **Angle** from the shortcut menu. Type 20 and press ENTER.

- Type 45 and press ENTER.

- Select the vertical line on the right-side. Next, select the horizontal and vertical lines, as shown in the figure.

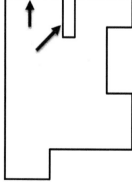

- Press ENTER to activate the **Chamfer** command. Next, select the horizontal and vertical lines, as shown.

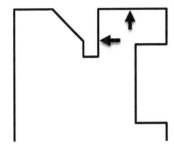

- Press ENTER to activate the **Chamfer** command. Right-click and select **Angle** from the shortcut menu.
- Type 20 and press ENTER.
- Type 30 and press ENTER. Select the vertical and horizontal lines, as shown in the figure.
- Press ENTER and select the vertical and horizontal lines, as shown in the figure.

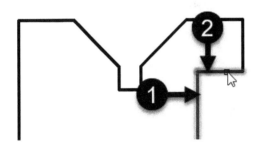 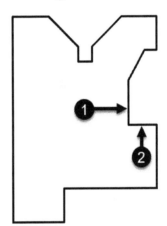

- Press ENTER to activate the **Chamfer** command.
- Right-click and select **Angle** from the shortcut menu. Type 65 and press ENTER.
- Type 15 and press ENTER. Select the horizontal and vertical lines, as shown in the figure.

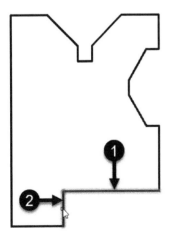

- Press ENTER to activate the **Chamfer** command.
- Right-click and select **Angle** from the shortcut menu. Type 7.5 and press ENTER.
- Type 75 and press ENTER. Select the horizontal and vertical lines, as shown in the figure.

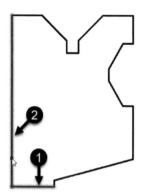

- Select the left vertical line and press **Delete**. Create a selection window across all the objects.

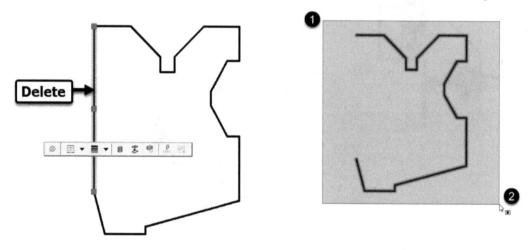

- Click **Copy** drop-down > **Mirror** on the **Modify** ribbon.
- Make sure that the **Ortho** mode is activated on the Status bar.
- Select the lower-left endpoint of the lines, as shown.
- Move the pointer upward and click to create the mirror line, as shown below.
- Select the points, as shown. The mirror line is defined.
- Type N and press ENTER. The selected objects are mirrored about the mirror line.

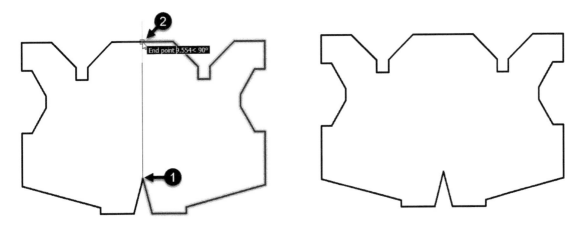

- Click **Polyline** drop-down > **Polygon** on the **Draw** panel.
- Type **5** as the number of sides and press ENTER.

- Right-click and select **Side Length**.

- Make sure that the **Ortho** button is activated on the Status bar.

- Click in the empty space. Next, move the pointer toward right. Type 40 and press ENTER.

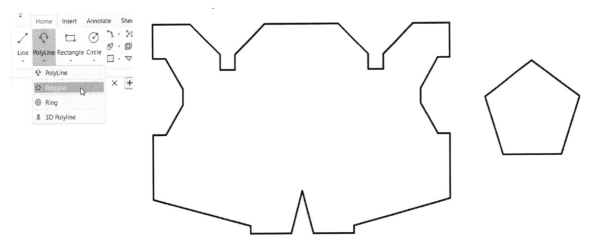

- Select the polygon and click the **Copy** drop-down > **Move** icon on the **Modify** panel of the **Home** ribbon tab.
- Select the vertex point of the polygon, as shown.
- Move the pointer and select the endpoint of the line, as shown.

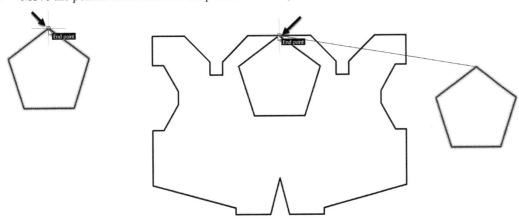

- Select the polygon and click the **Copy** drop-down > **Move** icon on the **Modify** panel of the **Home** ribbon tab.

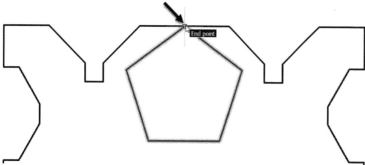

- Select the vertex point of the polygon, as shown.
- Move the pointer downward. Next, type 27.5 and press ENTER.

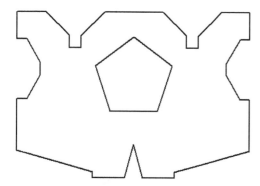

- Click **Line** drop-down > **Line** on the **Draw** toolbar. Next, deactivate the **Ortho** mode on the status bar.
- Select the vertices of the polygon, as shown.

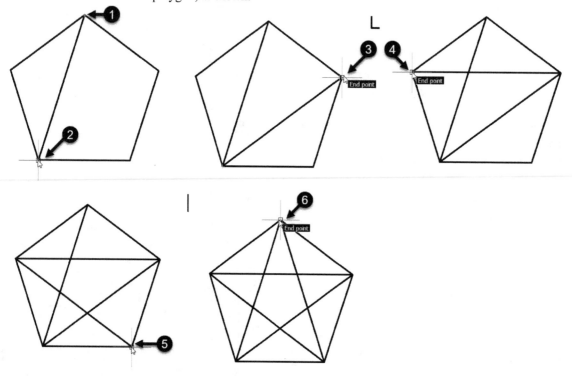

- Select the polygon and press Delete.

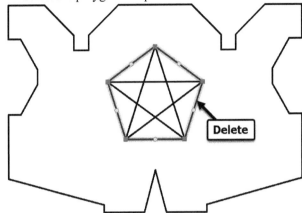

- Click **Trim** drop-down > **Trim** on the **Modify** panel. Next, press ENTER.

- Select the inner lines of the star, as shown.

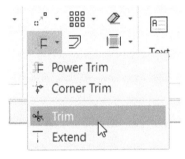 

- Press ESC.
- Save and close the drawing file.

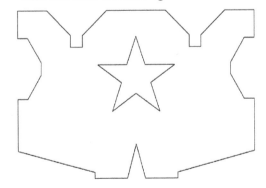

Tutorial 12

In this example, you will create the drawing shown in the figure.

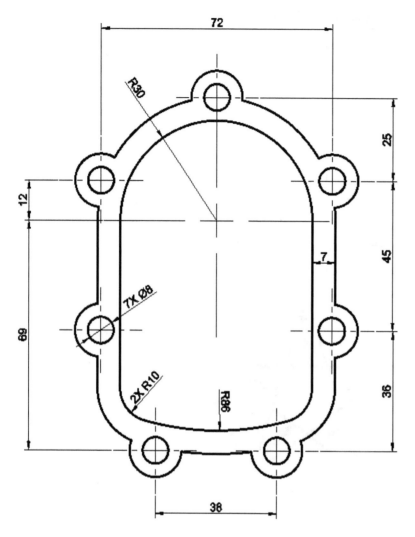

- Start a new drawing file.

- Activate the **Ortho** icon on the Status bar.
- Click **Circle** drop-down > **Circle** on the **Draw** panel on the **Home** ribbon tab. Next, pick a point in the graphics area.

- Type 86, and press ENTER.
- Press ENTER to activate the **Circle** command. Next, select the lower quadrant point of the existing circle.
- Type 30 and press ENTER.

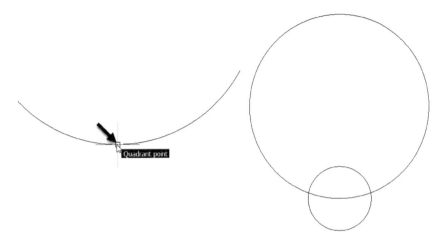

- Select the circle and click the **Copy** drop-down > **Move** icon on the **Modify** panel of the **Home** ribbon tab.
- Select the centerpoint of the small circle. Next, move the pointer upward, type 63 and press ENTER.

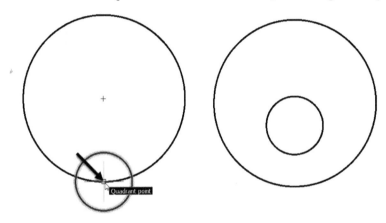

- On the **Draw** panel, click **Line** drop-down > **Line**. Next, select the left quadrant point of the small circle.
- Move the pointer downward and click outside the large circle.
- Likewise, create another line, as shown.

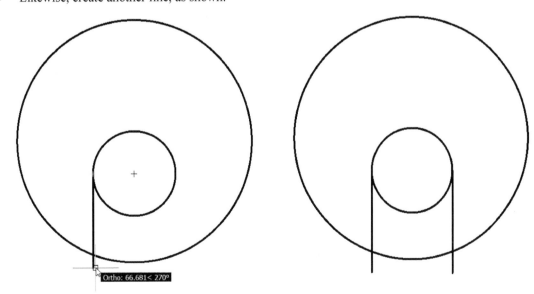

- Click **Home** tab > **Modify** panel > **Trim/Extend** drop-down > **Trim** on the ribbon.
- Press ENTER and select the entities, as shown below. Press ESC.

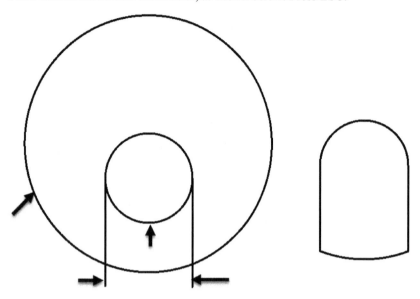

- On the ribbon, click **Home > Modify > Fillet**.
- Select the **Radius** option on the command window. Next, type in 10 — press Enter.
- Select the bottom arc and the left vertical line.
- Press ENTER and select the bottom arc and the right vertical line.

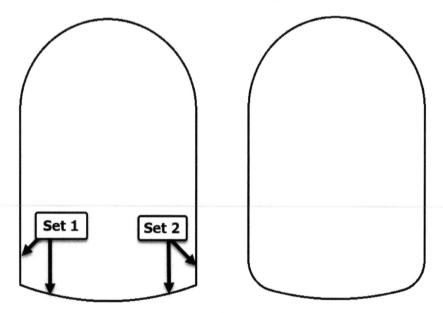

- On the ribbon, click **Home > Modify > Offset**. Next, type-in 7 in the command window and press Enter.
- Select the large arc. Click outside to create an offset arc.
- Likewise, offset the other entities, as shown below.

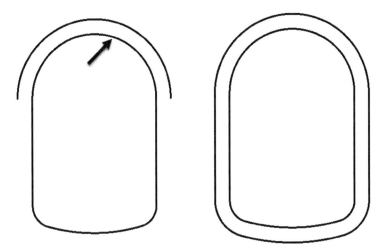

- Create two circles at the center point of the large arc. The diameters of the two circles are 16 mm and 8 mm, respectively.

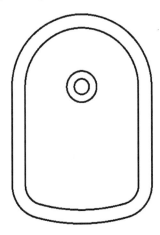

- Select the two newly created circles. Next, right-click and select **Move**.
- Select the centerpoint of the circles to define the base point.
- Move the pointer toward the left and type 36 and press ENTER.
- Again, select the circles. Next, right-click and select **Move**.
- Select the centerpoint of the circles.
- Move the pointer upward. Type 12 and press ENTER.

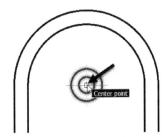 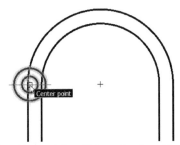 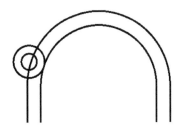

- Select the two newly created circles. Next, right-click and select **Copy**.
- Select the centerpoint of the circles to define the base point.
- Select the top quandrant point of the arc, as shown.

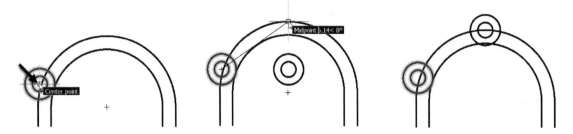

- Move the pointer downward, type 45 and press ENTER.

- Move the pointer downward, type 81 and press ENTER. Next, press ESC.

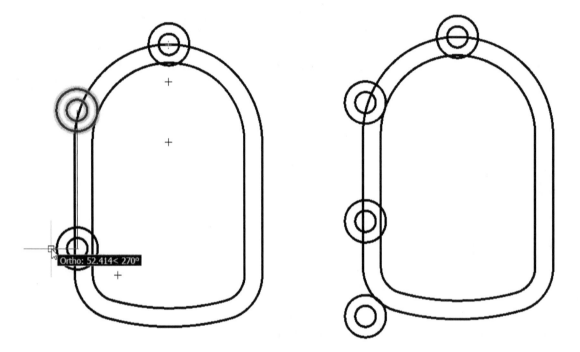

- Select the bottom circles. Next, right-click and select **Move**.

- Select the centerpoint of the selected circles. Next, move the pointer toward right, type 17, and then press ENTER.

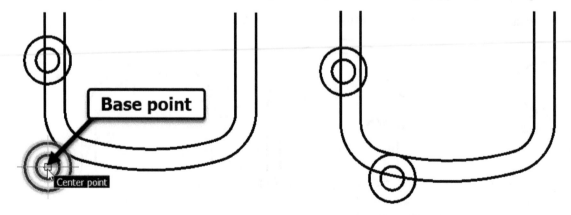

- On the ribbon, click **Home > Modify > Copy** drop-down > **Mirror**, and then select the circles, as shown. Press Enter to accept the selection.

- Define the mirror line by selecting the points, as shown below.

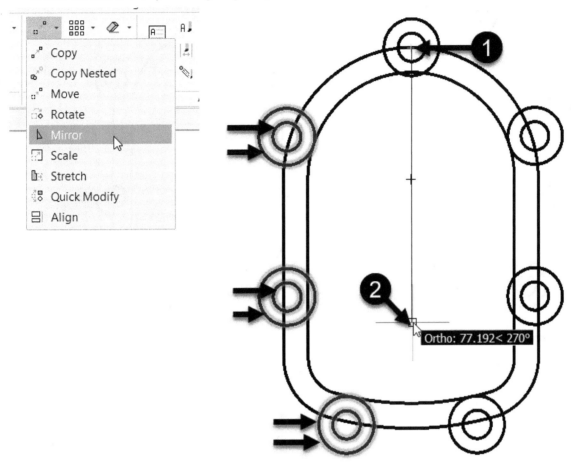

- Right-click and select **NO** to keep the original objects.

- Click **Trim** drop-down > **Trim** on the **Modify** panel. Next, select the outer loop of the drawing and press ENTER.

- Select the lower portions of the large circles, as shown.

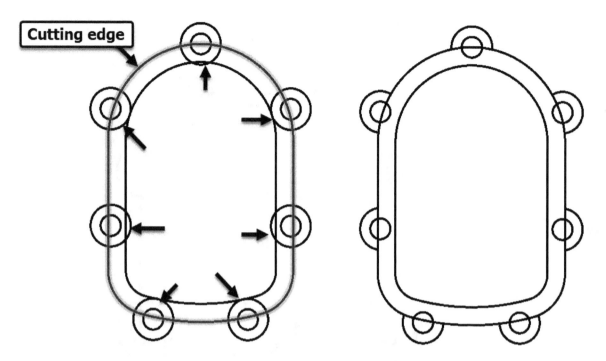

- Press ENTER twice and select the trimmed circles as the cutting edges, as shown.

- Select the portions of the arcs and lines to trim, as shown.

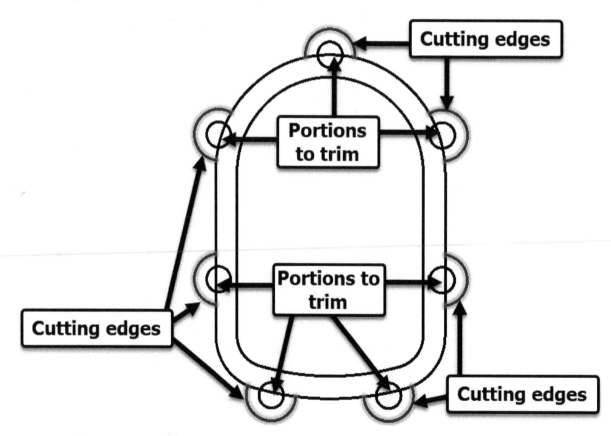

- Zoom to the bottom portion of the drawing and select the two untrimmed edges, as shown.

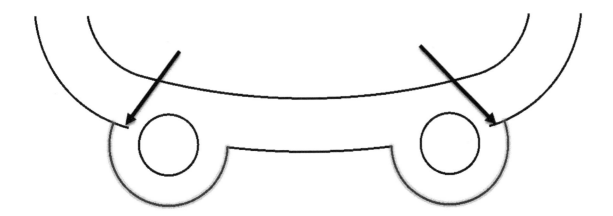

- Save and close the drawing file.

Tutorial 13

In this tutorial, you will draw the exhaust fan shown in figure.

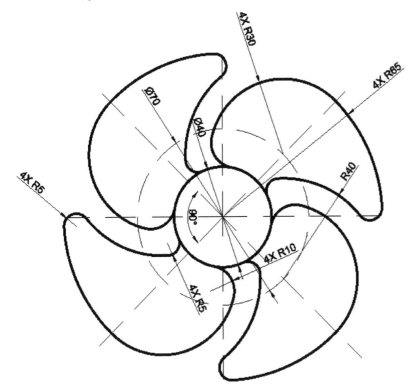

- Start a new CorelCAD file using the **standardiso** template. Next, set the **Workspace** to **Drafting and Annotation**.

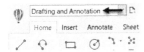

- Type **UN** in the command window and press Enter.

- On the **Drawing Settings** dialog, select **Type > Decimal** from the **Length** section.

- Select **Precision > 0.00**. Next, set the **Block units format** to **Millimeters**, and click **OK**.

- On the ribbon, click the **View** tab > **Navigate** panel > **Zoom** drop-down > **Zoom Bounds**.

- Deactivate the **Grid** icon on the status bar.

- On the **Home** tab, click the **Layers Manager** button on the **Layers** panel.

- On the **Layers Manager** dialog, click the **New** button.

- Type **Dimension** in the **Name** box and press Enter.

- Click the **LineWeight** drop-down of the **Dimension** layer and select **0.25 mm**.

- Click the **New** button and type **Construction** in the **Layer Name** box and press Enter.

- Select **0.15 mm** from the **LineWeight** drop-down of the **Construction** layer.

- Click the **LineStyle** drop-down of the **Construction** layer and select the **Other** option.

- On the **Line Style** dialog, click the **Load** button. The **Load Line Styles** dialog appears.

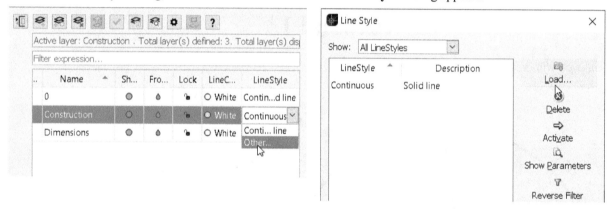

- On the **Load Line Styles** dialog, select the **DASHED** option and click **OK**.

- Select **DASHED** on the **Line Style** dialog and click **OK**.

- Close the **Layers Manager** Palette.

- On the ribbon, click **Home > Draw > Circle**. Click in the graphics window and move the pointer outwards.
- Type **20** in the **Radius** box and press Enter.

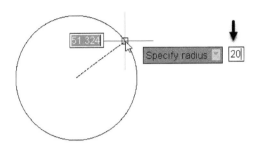

- Select the **Construction** layer from the **Layer Manager** drop-down on the **Layers** panel of the **Home** tab.
- Activate the **Circle** command.
- Press and hold the Shift key, right-click, and then select the **Center** option.
- Select the center point of the previous circle.
- Move the pointer and type **35** in the **Radius** box and press Enter.

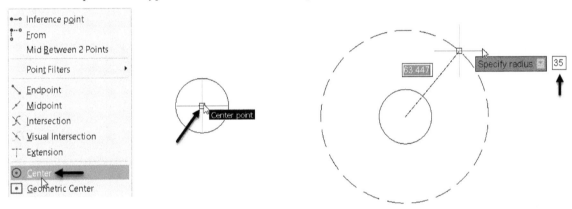

- On the ribbon, click **Home > Draw > Line**.
- Click on the center point of the circle and move the pointer upwards. Click to create a line, as shown.

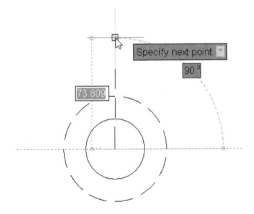

- Press Esc.

- On the ribbon, click **Home > Modify > Pattern**.

- Click the **Circular** tab on the **Pattern** dialog.

- Click the **Specify entities** button under the **Selection** section on the dialog.

- Select the vertical line and press Enter.

- Select the **Angle Between and Total Number of Elements** from the **Base pattern on** drop-down under the **Settings** section.

- Type **45** in the **Angle between** box and enter **8** in the **Total number**.

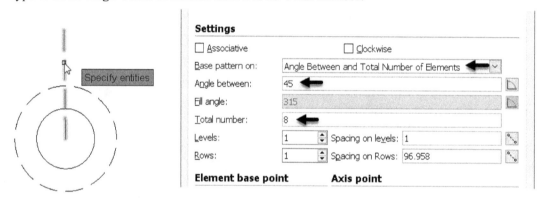

- Click the **Pick Center Point** button under the **Axis point** section.

- Select the center point of the circle, as shown.

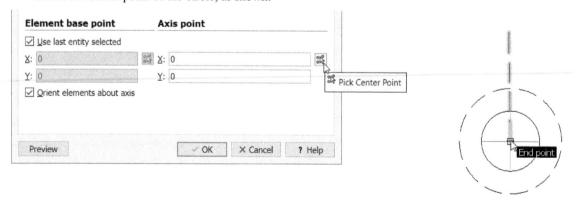

- Click **OK** on the **Pattern** dialog.

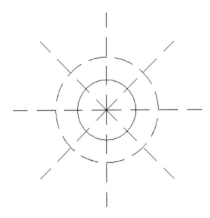

- On the **Layers** panel, select **0** from the **Layers Manager** drop-down.
- Activate the **Circle** command.
- Click on the intersection point of the large circle and the inclined line at the lower right corner, as shown.

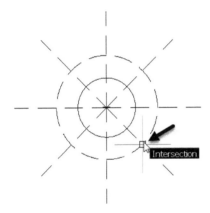

- Move the pointer and type **30** in the **Radius** box. Press Enter.
- Likewise, create another circle of radius **40** at the same intersection point, as shown.

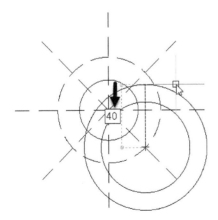

- On the ribbon, click **Home > Modify > Trim drop-down > Trim**.
- Select the inner circle and the inclined line, and then press ENTER.
- Select the unwanted portions, as shown.

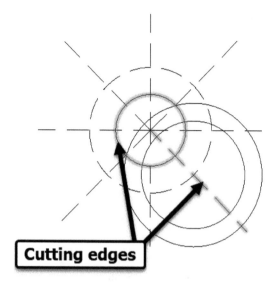

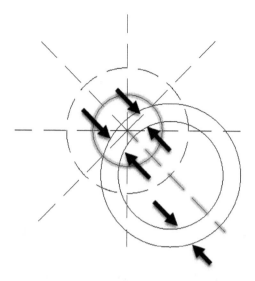

Cutting edges

- Press Esc.

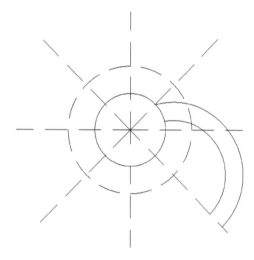

- Click the **Fillet** command on the **Home** tab of the **Modify** panel. Next, right-click and select **Radius**.
- Type-in **10** in the **Radius** box and press Enter. Select the small arc and select the small circle, as shown.

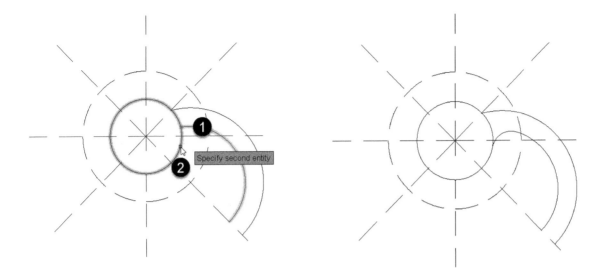

- Click **Home >Modify > Pattern** on the ribbon.

- Click the **Circular** tab on the **Pattern** dialog.

- Select the **Specify entities** button under the **Selection** section on the dialog.

- Select the arcs and fillet, as shown. Press Enter.

- Select the **Angle Between and Total Number of Elements** from the **Base pattern on** drop-down under the **Settings** section.

- Type-in **90** in the **Angle between** box and enter **4** in the **Total number** box.

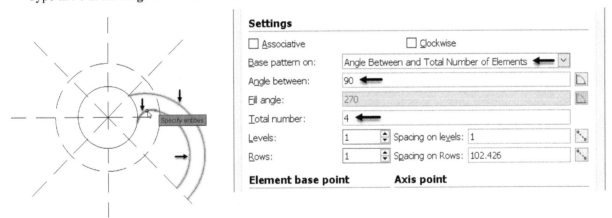

- Click the **Pick Center point** button under the **Axis point** section.

- Select the center point of the circle, as shown.

- Uncheck the **Associative** option and click **OK** on the **Pattern** dialog.

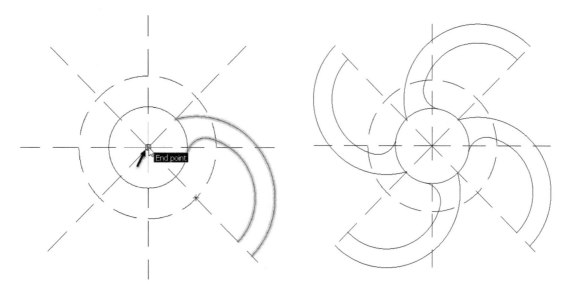

- On the **Home** tab, click the **Circle** command on the **Draw** panel.
- Click on the center point of the circle and move the pointer outwards.
- Type **65** in the **Radius** box and press Enter.

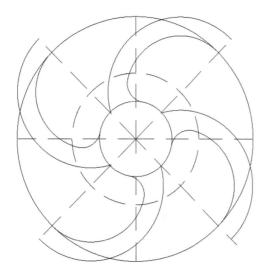

- Click **Home > Modify > Power trim** drop-down **> Trim** on the ribbon. Press Enter.
- Trim the unwanted portions, as shown.

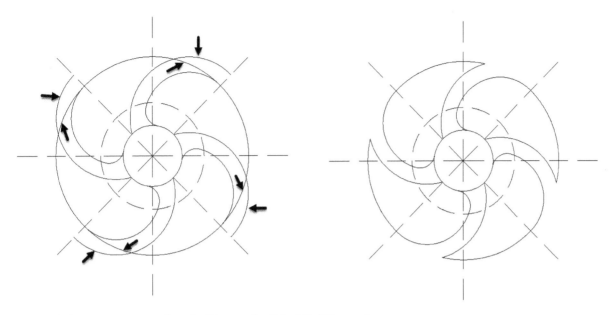

- Click the **Fillet** command on the **Home** tab of the **Modify** panel.
- Right-click and select **Radius**. Next, type **5** and press Enter.
- Select the large arc and the small arc, as shown.
- Likewise, fillet the other corners, as shown.

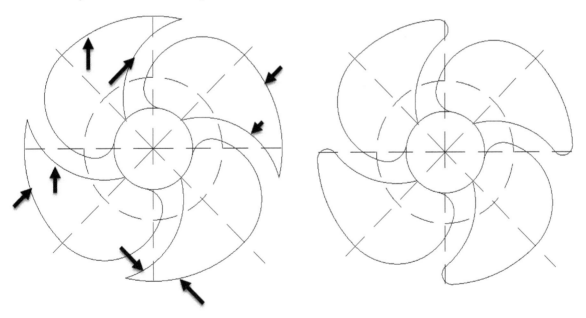

- Press Enter to activate the **Fillet** command.
- Select the arc and small circle, as shown. Likewise, create other fillets, as shown.

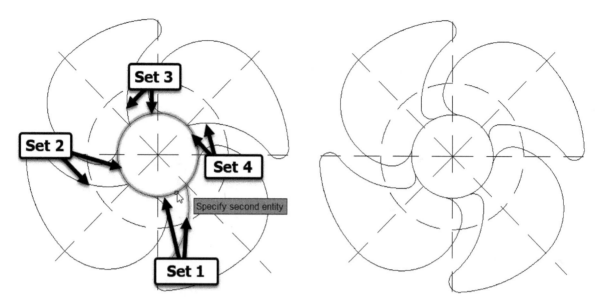

- Save and close the file.

Tutorial 14 (Creating Orthographic views)

Orthographic Views are standard representations of an object on a sheet. These views are created by projecting an object onto three different planes (top, front, and side planes). You can project an object by using two different methods: **First Angle Projection** and **Third Angle Projection**. The following figure shows the orthographic views that will be created when an object is projected using the **First Angle Projection** method.

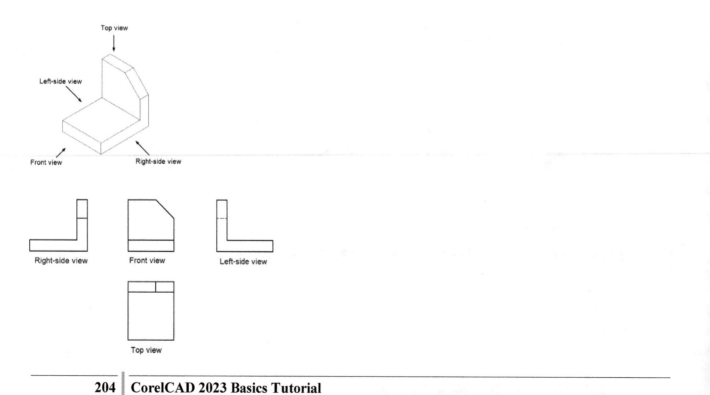

The following figure shows the orthographic views that will be created when an object is projected using the **Third Angle Projection** method.

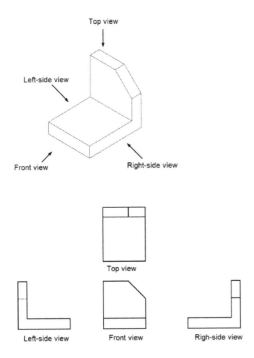

In this tutorial, you will create the orthographic views of the part shown below. The views will be created by using the **Third Angle Projection** method.

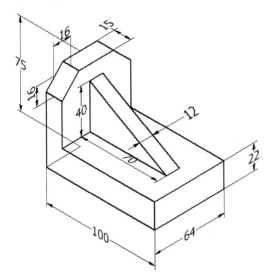

- Open a new drawing using the **standardiso** template.
- On the ribbon, click the **Home > Layers > Layers Manager**. It displays the Layer Manager.
- Create two new layers with the following properties.

Layer Name	Lineweight	LineStyle
Construction	0.00 mm	Continuous Solid Line
Object	0.30 mm	Continuous Solid Line

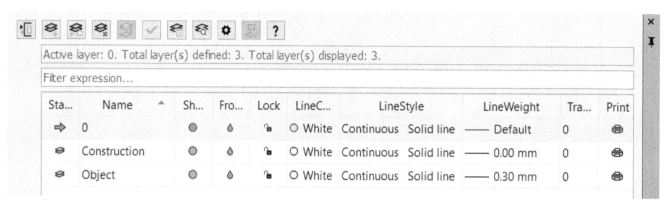

- Double-click in the Status column of the **Construction** layer to activate it.
- Close the **Layers Manager**.
- Activate the **Ortho** icon on the status bar.
- Click **View** > **Navigate** > **Zoom** > **Zoom Bound** on the ribbon.
- On the ribbon, click **Home** tab > **Draw** panel > **Line** drop-down > **Infinite Line**.
- Click anywhere in the lower left corner of the graphics window.
- Move the pointer upward and click to create a vertical construction line.
- Move the pointer toward the right and click to create a horizontal construction line.
- Press ENTER twice.
- Right-click and select Offset. Next, type 100 as the offset distance and press ENTER.
- Select the vertical construction line.
- Move the pointer toward the right and click to create an offset line.

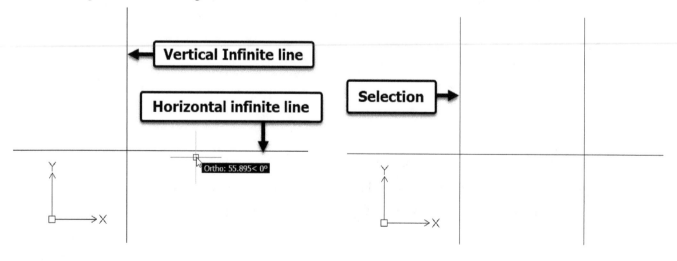

- Click **Draw > Modify > Offset** on the ribbon. Type 75 as the offset distance and press ENTER.

- Select the horizontal construction line. Move the pointer above and click to create the offset line.

- Press ENTER to exit the **Offset** tool.

- Likewise, create other offset lines as shown below. The offset dimensions are displayed in the image. Do not add dimensions to the lines.

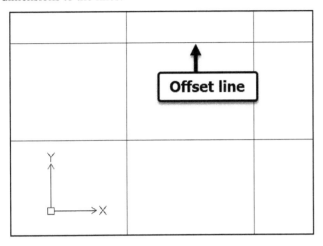
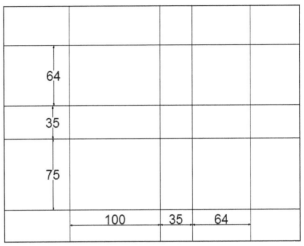

- Activate the **Object** layer. Next, activate the **LWeight** button on the status bar.

- Click the **Line** drop-down > **Line** on the **Draw** panel. Next, select the intersection points of the construction lines, as shown.

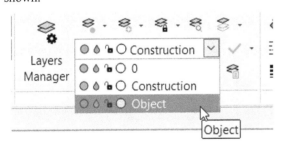
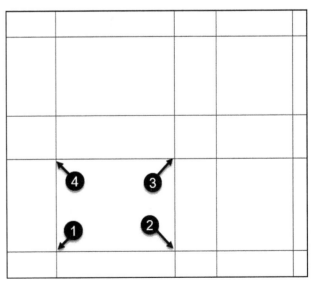

- Select the **Close** option from the shortcut menu to create the outline of the front view.

- Likewise, create the outlines of the top and side views.

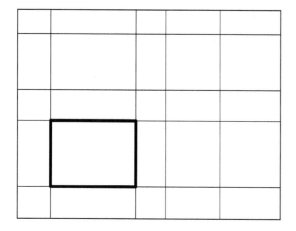

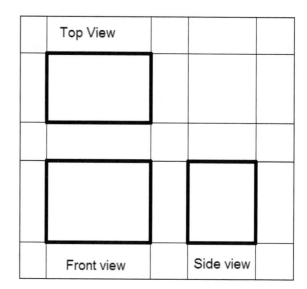

Next, you must turn off the **Construction** layer.

- Click on the **Layer** drop-down in the **Layers** panel.

- Click the green circle of the **Construction** layer; the layer will be turned off.

- Use the **Offset** tool and create two parallel lines on the front view, as shown below.

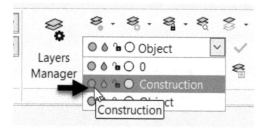

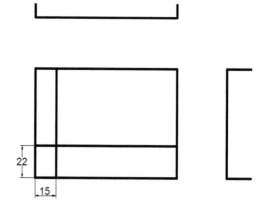

- Use the **Trim** tool and trim the unwanted lines of the front view as shown below.

- Use the **Offset** tool to create the parallel line as shown below.

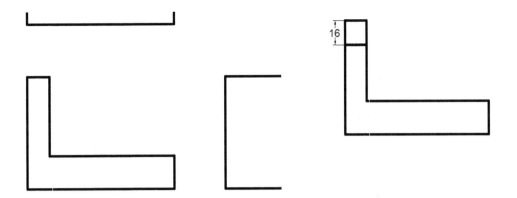

- Use the **Offset** tool and create offset lines in the Top view as shown below.
- Use the **Trim** tool and trim unwanted objects.

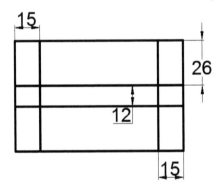

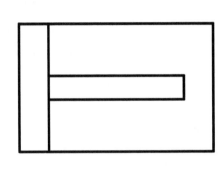

- Create other offset lines and trim the unwanted portions as shown below.

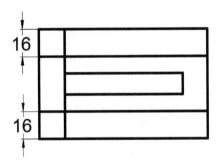

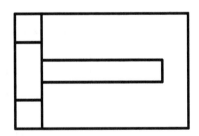

- Deactivate the **Ortho** icon on the status bar.
- Click the **Line** button on the **Draw** panel.
- Press and hold the SHIFT key and right-click. Select the **From** option.
- Select the endpoint of the line in the front view as shown below.
- Move the pointer on the vertical line and enter **40** in the command window; the first point of the line is specified at a point 40 mm away from the endpoint. Also, a rubber band line will be attached to the pointer.
- Move the pointer onto the endpoint on the top view as shown below.

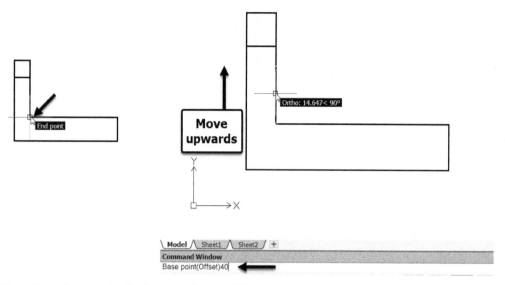

- Move the pointer vertically downward; you will notice the track lines.
- Move the pointer near the horizontal line of the front view and click at the intersection point as shown below. Press ENTER to exit the tool.

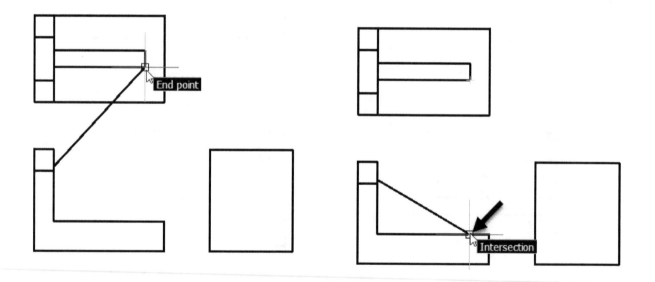

Next, you must create the right side view. To do this, you must draw a 45- degree miter line and project the measurements of the top view onto the side view.

- Click on the **Layer** drop-down in the **Layers** panel.
- Click the grey circle of the **Construction** layer; the **Construction** layer is turned on.
- Select the **Construction** layer from the **Layer** drop-down to set it as the current layer.
- Draw an inclined line by connecting the intersection points of the construction lines as shown below.

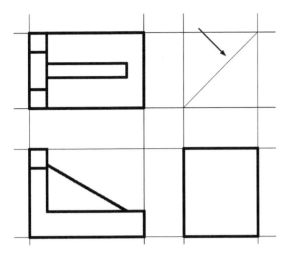

- Click the **Line** drop-down > **Infinite Line** on the **Draw** panel.

- Right-click and select the **Horizontal** option from the shortcut menu. Next, select the points on the top and front views, as shown below.

The projection lines are created, as shown below.

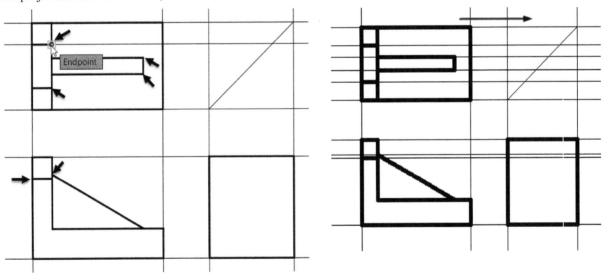

- Press ENTER twice.

- Right-click and select the **Vertical** option from the shortcut menu.

- Create the vertical projection lines as shown below.

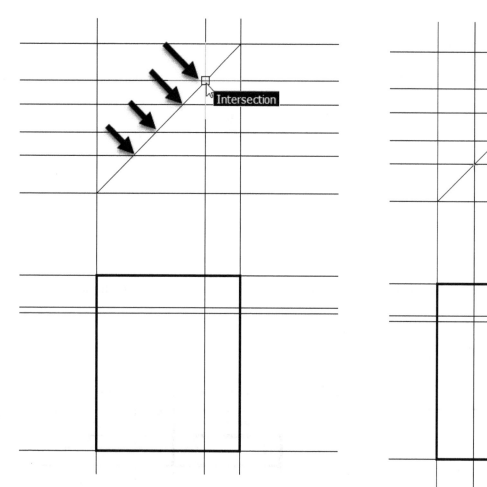

- Use the **Trim** tool and trim the extended portions of the infinite lines.

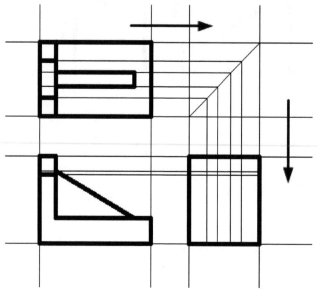

- Set the **Object** layer as current.

- Click the **Offset** button on the **Modify** panel. Next, right-click and select the **Through point** option from the shortcut menu.

- Select the lower horizontal line of the side view.

- Select the endpoint on the front view to define the through point, as shown below. Next, press ESC.

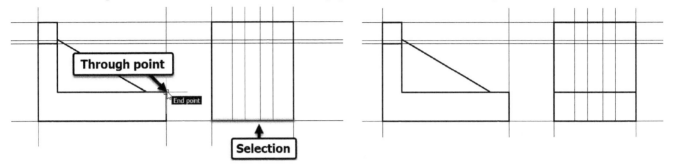

- Use the **Line** tool and create the objects in the side view as shown below.

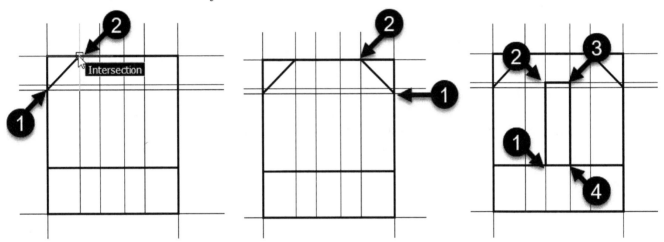

- Turn off the **Construction** layer by clicking on the green circle of the **Construction** layer.

- Trim the unwanted portions on the right side view.

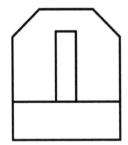

The drawing after creating all the views is shown below.

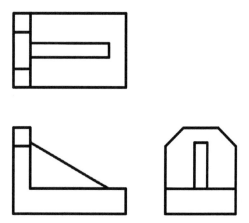

- Save the file as **ortho_views.dwg**. Close the file.

Tutorial 15 (Creating Auxiliary Views)

Most of the components are represented by using orthographic views (front, top and/or side views). But many components have features located on inclined faces. You cannot get the true shape and size for these features by using the orthographic views. To see an accurate size and shape of the inclined features, you must create an auxiliary view. An auxiliary view is created by projecting the component onto a plane other than horizontal, front or side planes. The following figure shows a component with an inclined face. When you create orthographic views of the component, you will not be able to get the true shape of the hole on the inclined face.

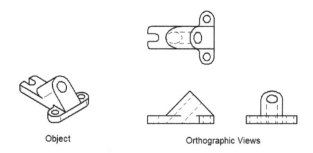

Object   Orthographic Views

To get the actual shape of the hole, you must create an auxiliary view of the object as shown below.

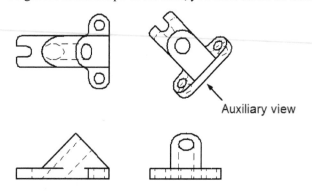

Auxiliary view

In this tutorial, you will create an auxiliary view of the object shown below.

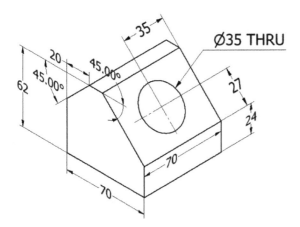

- Open a new CorelCAD file.
- Create four new layers with the following properties.

Layer Name	Lineweight	LineStyle
Construction	0.00 mm	Continuous
Object	0.50 mm	Continuous
Hidden	0.30 mm	HIDDEN
Centerline	0.30 mm	CENTER

- Select the **Construction** layer from the **Layers Manager** drop-down in the **Layers** panel.
- Create a rectangle at the lower left corner of the graphics window, as shown in the figure.

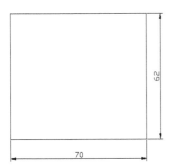

- Select the rectangle and click the **Copy** drop-down > **Copy** on the **Modify** panel.
- Select the lower left corner of the rectangle as the base point.
- Make sure that the **Ortho** mode is activated.
- Move the pointer upward and type **25** in the command window — next, press ENTER.
- Press ESC to exit the **Copy** tool.

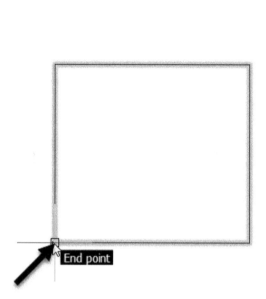

- Click the **Copy** drop-down > **Rotate** button on the **Modify** panel and select the copied rectangle. Press ENTER to accept.
- Select the lower right corner of the copied rectangle as the base point.
- Type 45 as the angle and press ENTER.

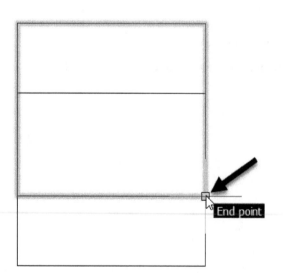

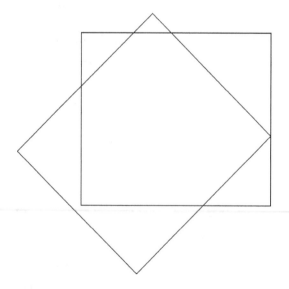

- Click the **ETrack** button on the Status Bar.
- Right-click on the **ESnap** button, and then select **Settings** from the shortcut menu.
- On the **Options** dialog, make sure that the **End** option is checked under the **Geometry Snaps** section. Next, click **OK**.
- Activate the **Rectangle** command.
- Place the pointer on the top left corner of the existing rectangle.

- Move the pointer vertically upward, and then notice a vertical tracking line from the top left corner of the rectangle.
- Move the pointer along the tracking line up to an approximate distance of 60 mm.
- Click to specify the first corner of the rectangle.
- Right-click and select **Dimensions** from the shortcut menu. Type 70 and press Enter to specify the length of the rectangle.
- Again, type 70 and press Enter to specify the width of the rectangle. Move the pointer up and click to position the rectangle.

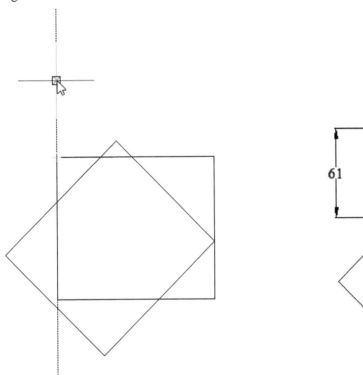

The rectangle located at the top is considered as top view and the below one as the front view.

- Click the **Explode** button on the **Modify** panel and select the newly created rectangle. Next, right-click to explode the rectangle.
- Activate the **Offset** tool. Right-click and select the **Through point** option from the shortcut menu.
- Select the left vertical line of the top rectangle.
- Select any one of the through points, as shown; the selected vertical line is offset through the selected point.
- Again, select the left vertical line.
- Move the pointer, and then select the remaining through point.

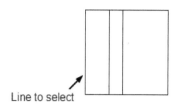

Line to select

Through points

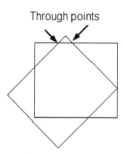

- Press Esc to deactivate the **Offset** tool.
- Select the **Object** layer from the **Layers Manager** drop-down in the **Layers** panel.
- Activate the **LWeight** button on the status bar.
- Activate the **Line** tool and select the intersection points on the front view, as shown.
- Likewise, create the object lines in the top view, as shown below.

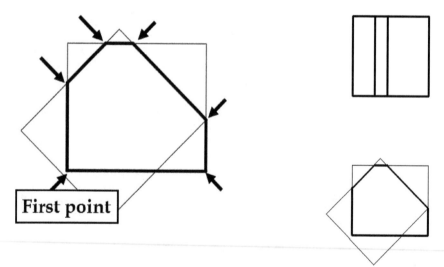

First point

- Select the **Construction** layer from the **Layers** panel.
- On the **Home** ribbon tab, click **Draw** panel > **Line** drop-down > **Infinite Line** tool.
- Right-click and select the **Offset** option from the shortcut menu. Next, right-click and select the **Specify position** option.
- Select the inclined line on the front view. Next, select the intersection point as shown below.

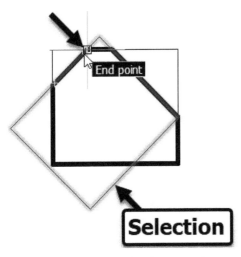

Selection

- Activate the **Offset** command and create other construction lines as shown below.

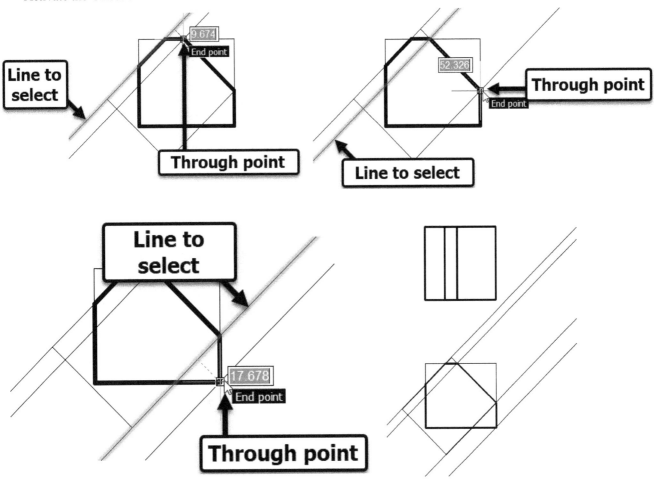

- Press Esc to deactivate the **Infinite Line** command.
- Activate the **Infinite Line** command. Right-click and select **Offset** from the shortcut menu.
- Type 80 and press ENTER. Select the inclined line of the front view, as shown.
- Move the pointer toward the right and click to create the construction line.

- Create other construction lines, as shown. The offset dimensions are given in the figure.

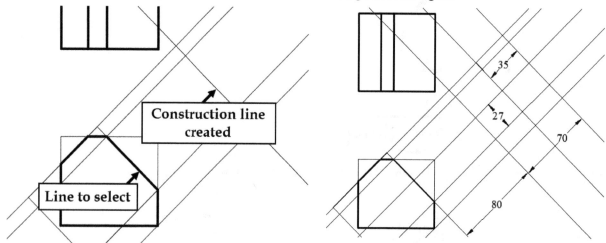

- Set the **Object** layer as the current layer. Next, create the object lines using the intersection points between the construction lines.
- Use the **Circle** tool and create a circle of 35 mm in diameter.
- Set the **Construction** layer as the current layer. Next, create projection lines from the circle.

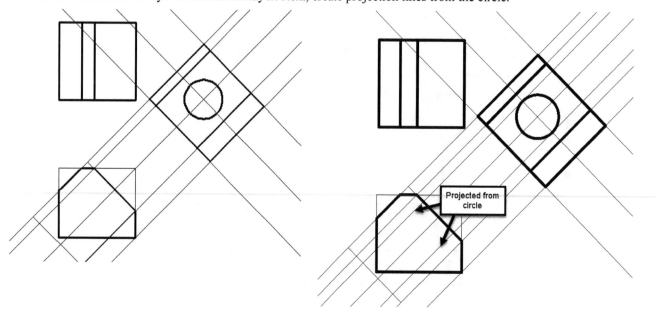

- Set the **Hidden** layer as the current layer. Next, create the hidden lines, as shown.
- Set the **Centerline** layer as the current layer.
- Activate the **Line** tool. Next, create the centerlines, as shown.

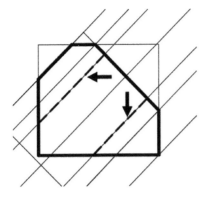
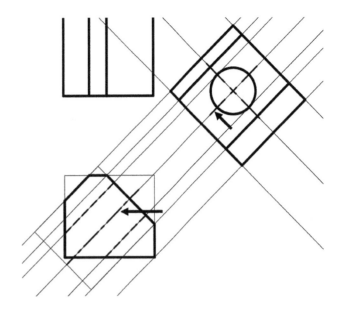

- Set the **Construction** layer as the current layer.
- On the ribbon, click **Home > Draw > Line** drop-down > **Ray**.
- Select the intersection point of the centerline and object line, as shown.
- Move the pointer upward and click to create a ray.
- Press ENTER twice.
- Likewise, create two more rays, as shown.

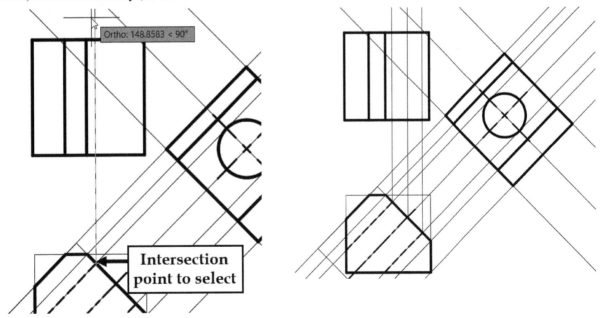

Ortho: 148.8583 < 90°

Intersection point to select

- Create a horizontal construction line passing through the midpoint of the top view, as shown.

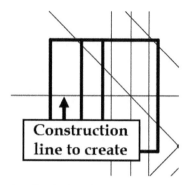

Construction
line to create

- Set the **Object** layer as the current layer,

- On the ribbon, click **Home > Draw > Ellipse drop-down > Axes**.

- Specify the first and second points, as shown. Move the point downward, type-in 17.5, and then press ENTER.

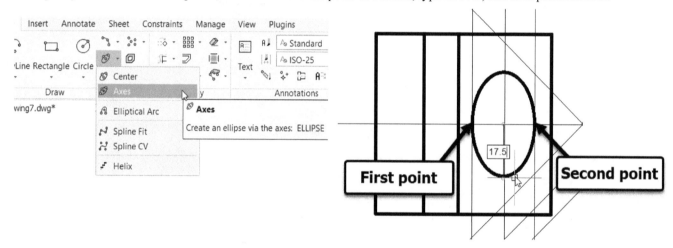

- Set the **Centerline** layer as current layer. Next, create the remaining centerlines.

- The drawing after hiding the **Construction** layer is shown next.

- Save the file as auxiliary_views.dwg.

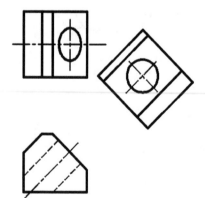

Tutorial 16 (Creating Named views)

While working with a drawing, you may need to perform numerous zoom and pan operations to view key portions of a drawing. Instead of doing this, you can save these portions with a name. Then, restore the named view and start working on them.

- Open the **ortho_views.dwg** file (The drawing file created in the Orthographic Views section of this chapter).
- To create a named view, click **View > Views > Named** on the ribbon; the **Views** dialog appears.

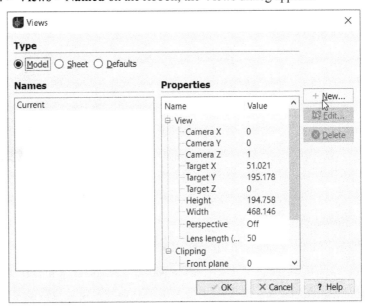

- Click the **New** button on the **Views** dialog; the **View** dialog appears.
- Select the **Specify in graphics area** option from the **Boundaries** section of the **View** dialog.
- Create a window on the front view, as shown below.
- Press ENTER to accept. Next, enter **Front** in the **View name** box.

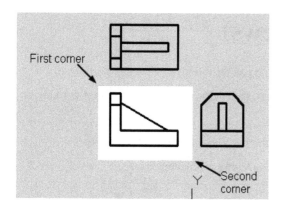

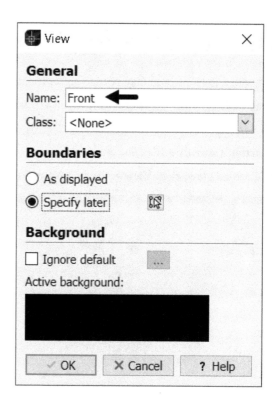

- Click **OK** on the **View** dialog.

- Likewise, create the named views for the top and right views of the drawing.

- To set the **Top** view to current, select it from the **Names** tree and click the **OK** button on the dialog; the **Top** view will be zoomed and fitted to the screen.

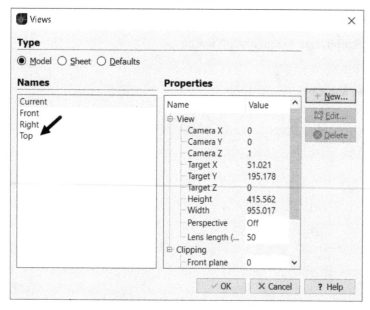

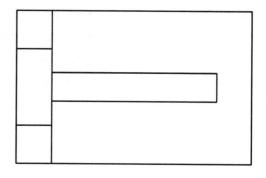

- Save and close the file.

Tutorial 17

In this example, you will create the drawing as shown in the figure and add dimensions to it.

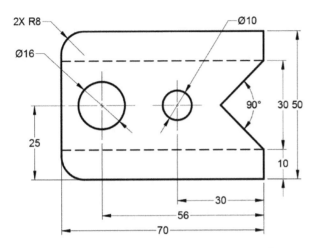

- Create four new layers with the following settings.

Layer	Lineweight	LineStyle
Construction	0.00 mm	Continuous
Object	0.50 mm	Continuous
Hidden	0.30 mm	HIDDEN
Dimensions	0.30 mm	Continuous

- Type LIMITS and press ENTER. Next, type 0,0 and press ENTER.
- Type 100, 100 and press ENTER to set the maximum limit of the drawing.
- On the ribbon, click **View > Navigate > Zoom Extents** drop-down > **Zoom Bounds**.
- Create the drawing on the **Object** and **Hidden** layers.

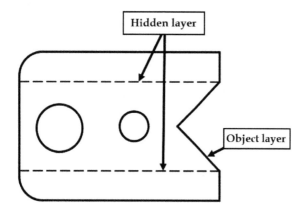

- Select the **Dimensions** layer from the **Layers Manager** drop-down in the **Layers** panel.

Creating a Dimension Style

The appearance of the dimensions depends on the dimension style that you use. You can create a new dimension style using the **Dimensions** settings on the **Options** dialog. In this dialog, you can specify various settings related to the appearance and behavior of dimensions. The following example helps you to create a dimension style.

- Right-click in the graphics window and select **Options**. Next, select the **Drafting Styles** option from the left side of the dialog.
- Expand the **Dimensions** node on the **Drafting styles** page.

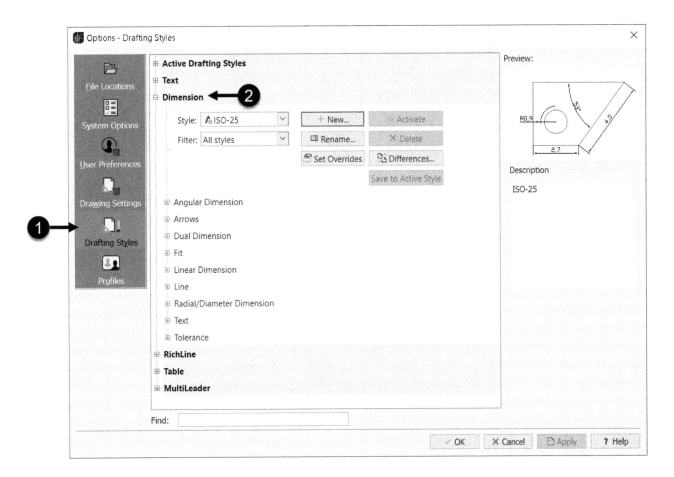

The basic nomenclature of dimensions is given below.

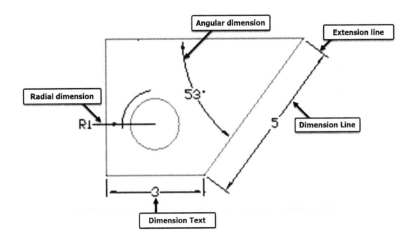

By default, the **ISO-25** or the **Standard** dimension style is active. If the default dimension style does not suit the dimensioning requirement, you can create a new dimension style and modify the nomenclature of the dimensions.

- To create a new dimension style, click the **New** button on the **Options** dialog; the **Create New DimensionStyle** dialog appears.
- In the **Create New DimensionStyle** dialog, enter **Mechanical** in the **Name**.

- Select **ISO-25** from the **Based on** drop-down and click **OK**.

- Expand the **Linear Dimension** node. Next, ensure that the **Format** is set to **Decimal**.

- Set **Precision** to **0**. Next, select **Decimal separator** > **'.'(Period)**.

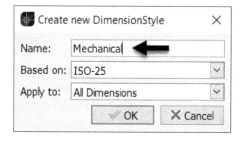

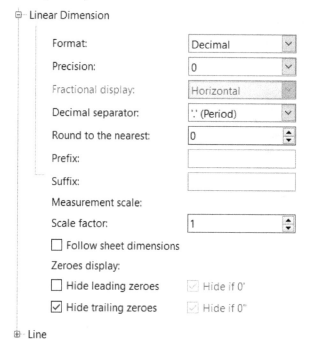

Study the other options in the **Linear Dimension** node. Most of them are self-explanatory.

- Expand the **Text** node. Next, expand the **Text settings** sub-node.

- Ensure that the **Height** is set **2.5**.

- In the **Text position** node, set the **Vertical** and **Horizontal** values to **Centered**.

- Select **Text alignment** > **Align horizontally**.

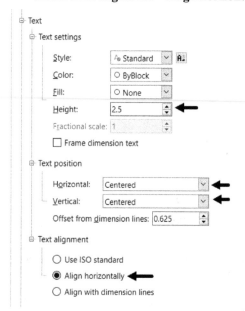

Study the other options in the **Text** node. These options let you change the appearance of the dimension text.

- Expand the **Line** node, and then expand the **Extension line settings** sub-node.Notice the two options: **Distance past dimension lines** and **Offset**.

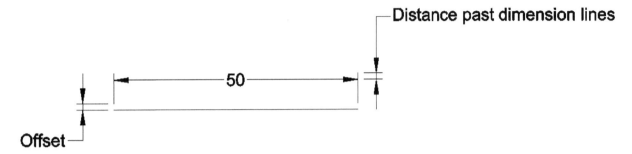

- Set **Distance past dimension line** and **Offset** to **1.25**.
- Set the **Offset** value in the **Dimension lines** settings node to **5**.

Study the different options in this node. The options in this tab are used to change the appearance and behavior of the dimension lines and extension lines.

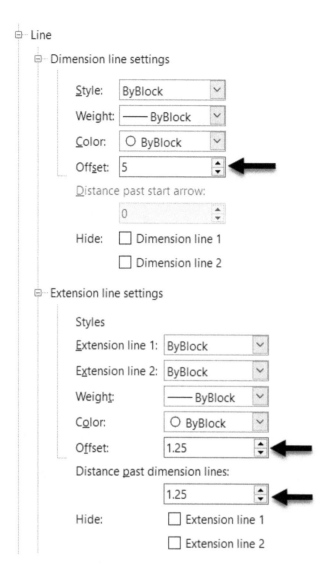

- Expand the **Arrows** node, and then set **Size** to 3. Notice the different options in this tab. The options in this tab are used to change the appearance of the arrows and symbols.

- Expand the **Radial/Diameter Dimension** > **Center mark display** node and enter 3 in the **Size** box.

- Select the **As Centerline** option.

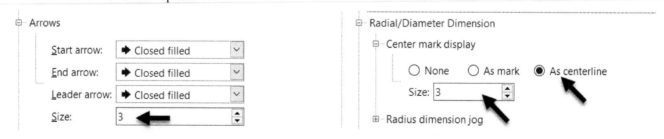

- Click **OK** to accept the settings.

- On the **Annotate** tab of the ribbon, click **Dimensions > CenterMark** .

- Select the circle from the drawing to apply the center mark to it. Next, press ENTER and select the remaining circle.

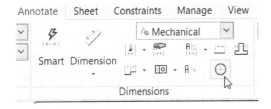

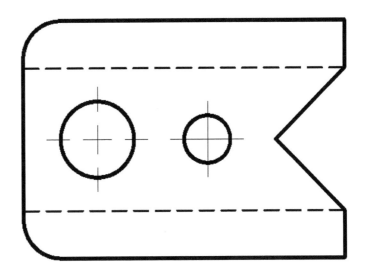

- On the ribbon, click **Annotate > Dimensions > Dimension** drop-down > **Linear**.

- Make sure that the **ESnap** button is turned on the status bar.

- Select the lower right corner of the drawing.

- Select the endpoint of the center mark of the small circle; the dimension is attached to the pointer.

- Move the pointer vertically downwards and position the dimension, as shown below.

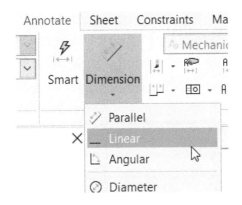

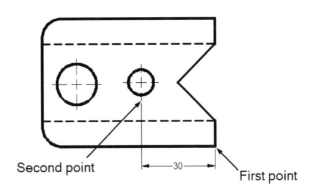

- On the ribbon, click **Annotate > Dimensions > Continue** drop-down > **Baseline**.

- Select the right extension line of the linear dimension if not already selected; a dimension is attached to the pointer.

- Select the endpoint of the center mark of the large circle; another dimension is attached to the pointer.

- Select the lower left corner of the drawing.

- Press ENTER twice.

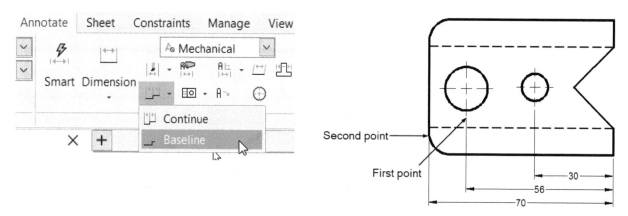

- On the ribbon, click **Annotate > Dimensions > Dimension** drop-down > **Angular**.

- Select the two angled lines of the drawing and position the angle dimension.

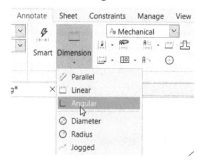

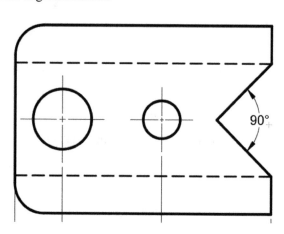

- On the ribbon, click **Annotate > Dimensions > Dimension** drop-down > **Diameter**.

- Select the large circle and position the diameter dimension, as shown.

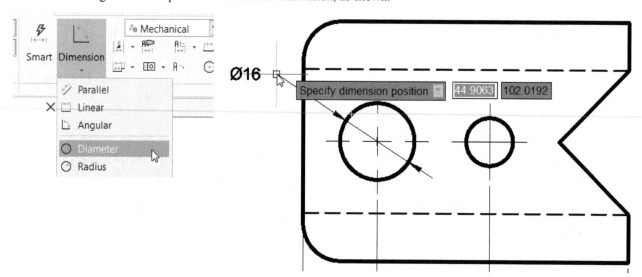

- Press ENTER and select the small circle and position the dimension.

- On the ribbon, click **Annotate > Dimensions > Dimension** drop-down > **Radius**.

- Select the fillet located at the top left corner. Next, position the radial dimension approximately at 45 degrees.

- Click on the palette button. Next, type 2X in the **Prefix Text** box, and then press the SPACEBAR.

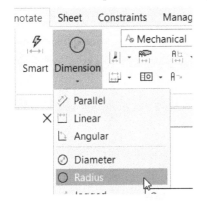 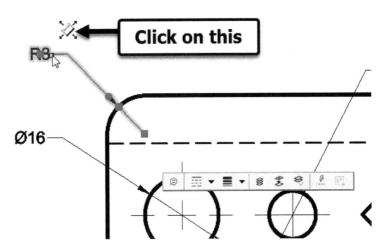

- Click in the graphics window to update the dimension text.

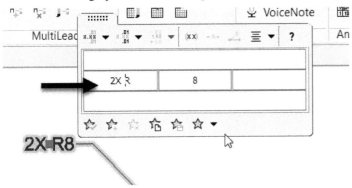 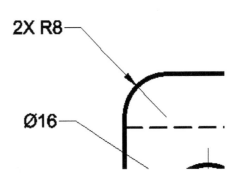

- Likewise, apply the other dimensions, as shown.

- Save and close the drawing.

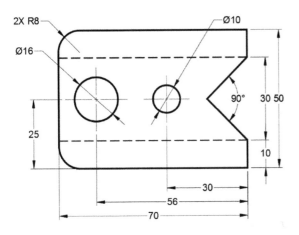

Tutorial 18 (Adding Dimensional Tolerances)

During the manufacturing process, the accuracy of a part is an important factor. However, it is impossible to manufacture a part with the exact dimensions. Therefore, while applying dimensions to a drawing, we provide some dimensional tolerances, which lie within acceptable limits. The following example shows you to add dimension tolerances in CorelCAD.

Example:

- Create the drawing, as shown below. Do not add dimensions to it.

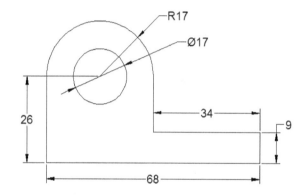

- Create a new dimension style with the name **Tolerances**.
- In the **Option – Drafting styles** dialog, expand the **Tolerances** node.
- In the **Tolerances** node, set the **Calculation** to **Deviation**.
- Set **Precision** to **0.00**.
- Set the **Maximum Value** and **Minimum Value** to **0.05**.
- Set the **Vertical text justification** to **Middle**.
- Specify the following settings in the **Linear Dimension**, **Text**, **Arrows**, and **Radial/Diameter Dimension** node:

    The **Linear Dimension** node:
    Format: Decimal
    Precision: 0.00
    Decimal Separator: '.'Period

    The **Text** node:
    Text settings:
        Height: 2.5
    Text position:
        Vertical:Centered
        Horizontal:Centered
    Text alignment: Align horizontal

The **Arrows** node:

Size: 2.5

The **Radial/Diameter Dimension** node:

*The **Center mark display** sub-node:*

As Centerline

Size: 2.5

- Click **Activate** on **Option – Drafting style** dialog. Click **OK** on the **Option – Drafting style** dialog.
- Apply dimensions to the drawing.

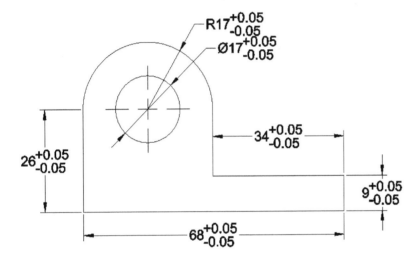

Tutorial 19 (Geometric Dimensioning and Tolerancing)

Earlier, you have learned how to apply tolerances to the size (dimensions) of a component. However, the dimensional tolerances are not sufficient for manufacturing a component. You must give tolerance values to its shape, orientation, and position as well. The following figure shows a note which is used to explain the tolerance value given to the shape of the object.

Note: The vertical face should not taper
over 0.08 from the horizontal face

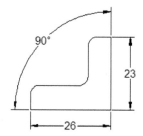

Providing a note in a drawing may be confusing. To avoid this, we use Geometric Dimensioning and Tolerancing (GD&T) symbols to specify the tolerance values to shape, orientation and position of a component. The following figure shows the same example represented by using the GD&T symbols. In this figure, the vertical face to which the tolerance frame is connected must be within two parallel planes 0.08 apart and perpendicular to the datum reference (horizontal plane).

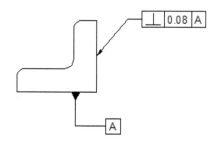

The Geometric Tolerancing symbols that can be used to interpret the geometric conditions are given in the table below.

Purpose		Symbol
To represent the shape of a single feature.	Straightness	⎯
	Flatness	▱
	Cylindricity	⌭
	Circularity	○
	Profile of a surface	⌒

	Profile of a line	⌒
To represent the orientation of a feature with respect to another feature.	Parallelism	//
	Perpendicularity	⊥
	Angularity	∠
To represent the position of a feature with respect to another feature.	Position	⊕
	Concentricity and coaxiality	◎
	Run-out	↗
	Total Run-out	↗↗
	Symmetry	≡

In this tutorial, you will apply geometric tolerances to the drawing shown below.

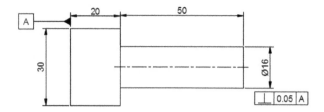

- Create the drawing as shown below.

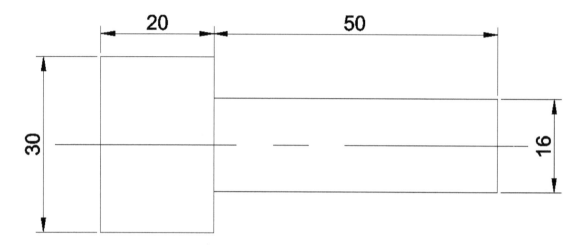

- Select the right vertical line and click on the palette button. Next, type %%c in the **Prefix Text** box.

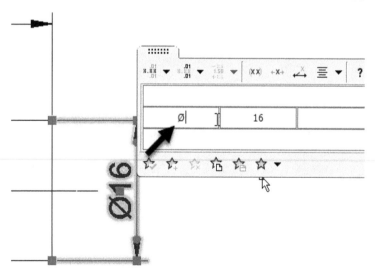

- Click **Annotate > Dimensions > Tolerance** on the ribbon; the **Geometric Tolerance** dialog appears.
- In the **Geometric Tolerance** dialog, click the **Sym** drop-down and select the **Perpendicularity** symbol.

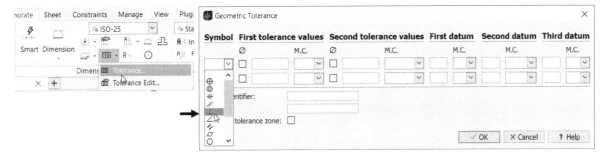

- Check the diameter option. Next, enter **.05** in the box next to the diameter symbol.

- Enter **A** in the **Datum identifier** box.

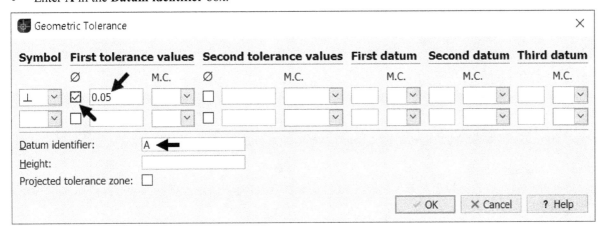

- Click **OK** and position the **Feature Control frame** as shown below.

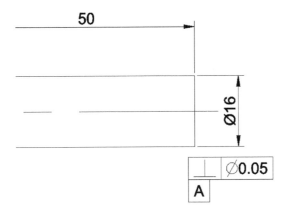

Next, you must add the datum reference.

- On the **Annotate** ribbon tab, expand the **Multileader** panel and click **Multileader Style**.

- Click the **New** button.

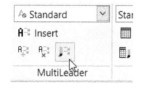

- On the **Create New MultiLeaderStyle** dialog, type **Tolerance** in the name box, and click **OK**.

- Expand the **Format** node and select **Arrowhead Settings > Arrow Style > Datum triangle filled**.
- Set the **Size** to 2.5.

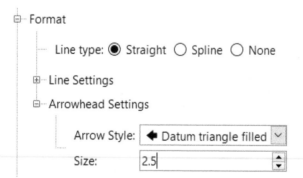

- In the **Settings** node, under the **Vertex** sub-node, set **Vertex Maximum** to **2**.
- Expand the **Contents** node and select **Multileader type > Tolerance**.
- Click the **Activate** button. Next, click **OK**.
- On the **Annotate** ribbon tab, click **Multileader > Insert**. Specify the first and second points of the datum reference as shown.
- On the **Geometric Tolerance** dialog, type **A** in the **Datum identifier** box.
- Click **OK**.

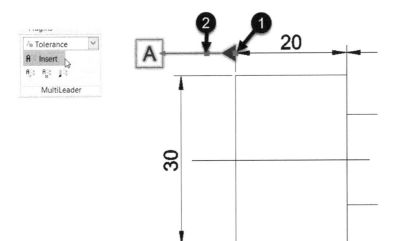

Printed in the USA
CPSIA information can be obtained
at www.ICGtesting.com
LVHW081947271023
762373LV00013B/1407